CHOOSING HEALTH HIGH SCHOOL

COMMUNICATION AND SELF-ESTEEM

Susan J. Laing, MS, CHES
Clint E. Bruess, EdD, CHES

ETR Associates
Santa Cruz, California
1997

ETR Associates (Education, Training and Research) is a nonprofit organization committed to fostering the health, well-being and cultural diversity of individuals, families, schools and communities. The publishing program of ETR Associates provides books and materials that empower young people and adults with the skills to make positive health choices. We invite health professionals to learn more about our high-quality publishing, training and research programs by contacting us at P.O. Box 1830, Santa Cruz, CA 95061-1830, (800) 321-4407.

Susan J. Laing, MS, CHES, is Associate Chief of Staff for Education at the Birmingham VA Medical Center. She has taught high school education, worked at the Oregon Department of Education, and served as a school district health education coordinator in Alaska. She has written instructor's manuals for college health texts and several high school health curricula.

Clint E. Bruess, EdD, CHES, is Dean of the School of Education at the University of Alabama at Birmingham. Formerly, he was Director of the School Health Education Project of the National Center for Health Education. He has published a number of articles in national health education journals and is the coauthor of *Implementing Comprehensive School Health; Sexuality Education: Theory and Practice; Decisions for Health;* and *Sexuality: Insights and Issues.*

Choosing Health High School
    Abstinence
    Body Image and Eating Disorders
    Communication and Self-Esteem
    Fitness and Health
    STD and HIV
    Sexuality and Relationships
    Tobacco, Alcohol and Drugs
    Violence and Injury

Series Editor: Kathleen Middleton, MS, CHES
Text design: Graphic Elements
Illustrations: Ann Smiley

Printed in the United States of America

10 9 8 7 6 5 4 3 2
ISBN 1-56071-521-9

Title No. H683

CONTENTS

Program Overview

Components . . . . **ix**

Teaching Strategies . . . . **xi**

Skills Infusion . . . . **xiii**

Working with Families and Communities . . . . **xiv**

The Communication and Self-Esteem Resource Book

Why Teach About Communication and Self-Esteem? . . . . **xv**

Objectives . . . . **xvi**

Anatomy of a Unit

Preparing to Teach . . . . **xvii**

Teaching the Activities . . . . **xviii**

Special Features . . . . **xix**

Evaluation Features . . . . **xx**

Unit 1: Influences on Health Behavior **2**

Unit Overview **3**

Activities

    1—The Murder of Crabwell Grommet **4**

    2—Influences on Health Behavior **6**

    3—Changing Health Habits **7**

Evaluation **8**

Information for Teachers

    Influences on Health Behavior *Instant Expert* **10**

CONTENTS

Unit 2: Who Am I? **16**

    Unit Overview **17**

    Activities

        1—Different and Special **18**

        2—Facts About Mental Health **19**

        3—Name Portraits **20**

        4—Characteristics of Mental Health **21**

        5—The Self-Esteem of Crabwell Grommet **23**

    Evaluation **24**

    Information for Teachers

        Self-Esteem and Mental Health *Instant Expert* **25**

Unit 3: Promoting Positive Self-Esteem **30**

    Unit Overview **31**

    Activities

        1—Assessing Self-Esteem **32**

        2—Promoting Self-Esteem **33**

        3—Positive Attributes **34**

        4—Improving Crabwell's Self-Esteem **35**

    Evaluation **36**

    Information for Teachers

        Promoting Self-Esteem *Instant Expert* **37**

Unit 4: Step by Step **42**

    Unit Overview **43**

    Activities

        1—What's the Problem? **44**

        2—The Decision-Making Process **45**

        3—The Decision Tree **46**

        4—Decision-Making Dilemmas **48**

    Evaluation **50**

    Information for Teachers

        Problem Solving and Decision Making *Instant Expert* **51**

CONTENTS

Unit 5: Types of Communication **54**

    Unit Overview **55**

    Activities

        1—Psst, Pass It On! **56**

        2—Types of Communication **57**

        3—What Do You See? **58**

        4—Nonverbal Communication **60**

        5—Communicating with Crabwell Grommet **61**

    Evaluation **62**

    Information for Teachers

        Types of Communication *Instant Expert* **64**

Unit 6: Promoting Communication **68**

    Unit Overview **69**

    Activities

        1—Communication Gap **70**

        2—Unsuccessful Communication **72**

        3—Successful Communication **74**

        4—Practicing Effective Communication **76**

        5—Measuring Assertiveness **77**

    Evaluation **79**

    Information for Teachers

        Effective Communication *Instant Expert* **80**

Final Evaluation **87**

Appendixes

Why Comprehensive School Health? **91**

Components of a Comprehensive Health Program **92**

The Teacher's Role **93**

Teaching Strategies **94**

Glossary **103**

References **107**

CONTENTS

Masters

Unit 1   **1.1**   The Murder of Crabwell Grommet

  1.2   Health Habit to Change

  1.3   Health Habit to Change Example

Unit 2   **2.1**   Self-Esteem and Mental Health

  2.2   Name Portrait

  2.3   Name Portrait Example

  2.4   Characteristics of Mental Health

Unit 3   **3.1**   Self-Esteem Assessment

  3.2   Self-Esteem Log

Unit 4   **4.1**   Problem-Solving Steps

  4.2   Problem-Solving Skills

  4.3   Decision Tree Example

  4.4   Decision Tree

  4.5   Decision-Making Dilemmas

Unit 5   **5.1**   Types of Communication

  5.2   What Do You See? (1)

  5.3   What Do You See? (2)

  5.4   What Do You See? (3)

Unit 6   **6.1**   The Communication Gap

  6.2   Unsuccessful Communication

  6.3   Successful Communication

  6.4   Measure Your Assertiveness

  6.5   What Would You Say?

ACKNOWLEDGMENTS

Choosing Health High School was made possible with the assistance of dedicated curriculum developers, teachers and health professionals. This program evolved from *Entering Adulthood*, the high school component of the *Contemporary Health Series*. The richness of this new program is demonstrated by the pool of talented professionals involved in both the original and the new versions.

Developers

Nancy Abbey
ETR Associates
Santa Cruz, California

Clint E. Bruess, EdD, CHES
University of Alabama at Birmingham
Birmingham, Alabama

Dale W. Evans, HSD, CHES
California State University, Long Beach
Long Beach, California

Susan C. Giarratano, EdD, CHES
California State University, Long Beach
Long Beach, California

Betty M. Hubbard, EdD, CHES
University of Central Arkansas
Conway, Arkansas

Lisa K. Hunter, PhD
Health & Education Communication Consultants
Berkeley, California

Susan J. Laing, MS, CHES
Department of Veterans Affairs Medical Center
Birmingham, Alabama

Donna Lloyd-Kolkin, PhD
Health & Education Communication Consultants
New Hope, Pennsylvania

Jeanie M. White, EdM, CHES
Education Consultant
Keizer, Oregon

Reviewers and Consultants

Brian Adams
Family Planning Council of Western Massachusetts
Northampton, Massachusetts

Janel Siebern Bartlett, MS, CHES
Dutchess County BOCES
Poughkeepsie, NY

Lori J. Bechtel, PhD
Pennsylvania State University, Altoona Campus
Altoona, Pennsylvania

Judith M. Boswell, RN, MS, CHES
University of New Mexico
Albuquerque, New Mexico

Marika Botha, PhD
Lewis and Clark State College
Lewiston, Idaho

Wanda Bunting
Newark Unified School District
Newark, California

John Daniels
Golden Sierra High School
Garden Valley, California

Joyce V. Fetro, PhD, CHES
San Francisco Unified School District
San Francisco, California

Mark L. Giese, EdD, FACSM
Northeastern State University
Tahlequah, Oklahoma

Karen Hart, MS, CHES
San Francisco Unified School District
San Francisco, California

Janet L. Henke
Old Court Middle School
Randallstown, Maryland

Russell G. Henke, MEd
Montgomery County Public Schools
Rockville, Maryland

Jon W. Hisgen, MS
Pewaukee Public Schools
Waukesha, Wisconsin

Bob Kampa
Gilroy High School
Gilroy, California

Freya Klein Kaufmann, MS, CHES
New York Academy of Medicine
New York, New York

David M. Macrina, PhD
University of Alabama at Birmingham
Birmingham, Alabama

Linda D. McDaniel, MS
Van Buren Middle School
Van Buren, Arkansas

Robert McDermott, PhD
University of South Florida
Tampa, Florida

ACKNOWLEDGMENTS

Carole McPherson, MA
Mentor Teacher Mission Hill Junior High School
Santa Cruz, California

Robert Mischell, MD
University of California, Berkeley
Berkeley, California

Donna Muto, MS
Mount Ararat School
Topsham, Maine

Priscilla Naworski, MS, CHES
California Department of Education
Healthy Kids Resource Center
Alameda County Office of Education
Alameda, California

Norma Riccobuono
La Paloma High School
Brentwood, California

Mary Rose-Colley, DEd, CHES
Lock Haven University
Lock Haven, Pennsylvania

Judith K. Scheer, MEd, EdS, CHES
Contra Costa County Office of Education
Walnut Creek, California

Michael A. Smith, MS, CHES
Long Beach Unified School District
Long Beach, California

Janet L. Sola, PhD
YWCA of the U.S.A.
New York, New York

Susan K. Telljohnn, HSD
University of Toledo
Toledo, Ohio

Donna J. Underwood, MS
Consulting Public Health Administrator
Champaign, Illinois

Peggy Woosley
Stuttgart Public Schools
Stuttgart, Arkansas

Dale Zevin, MA
Educational Consultant
Watsonville, California

PROGRAM OVERVIEW

COMPONENTS

> ### PROGRAM GOAL
> Students will acquire the necessary skills and information to make healthy choices.

Choosing Health High School consists of 8 Teacher/Student Resource books in critical topics appropriate for the high school health curriculum. *Think, Choose, Act Healthy, High School* provides creative activities to augment the basic program. There are also 13 *Health Facts* books that provide additional content information for teachers.

- **Teacher/Student Resource Books**—These 8 books address key health topics, content and issues for high school students. All teacher/student information, instructional process, assessment tools and student activity masters for the particular topic are included in each book.

- ***Think, Choose, Act Healthy, High School***—This book provides 150 reproducible student activities that work hand in hand with the teacher/student resource books. They will challenge students to think and make their own personal health choices.

- *Health Facts* **Books**—These reference books provide clear, concise background information to support the resource books.

PROGRAM OVERVIEW

Health Facts Books Correlation	
Resource Books	***Health Facts* Books**
Abstinence	Abstinence Sexuality
Body Image and Eating Disorders	Nutrition and Body Image
Communication and Self-Esteem	Self-Esteem and Mental Health
Fitness and Health	Fitness
STD and HIV	STD HIV Disease
Sexuality and Relationships	Sexuality
Tobacco, Alcohol and Drugs	Drugs Tobacco
Violence and Injury	Violence Injury Prevention

PROGRAM OVERVIEW

TEACHING STRATEGIES

Each resource book is designed so you can easily find the instructional content, process and skills. You can spend more time on teaching and less on planning. Special tools are provided to help you challenge your students, reach out to their families and assess student success.

A wide variety of learning opportunities is provided in each book to increase interest and meet the needs of different kinds of learners. Many are interactive, encouraging students to help each other learn. The **31** teaching strategies can be divided into 4 categories based on educational purpose. They are Informational, Creative Expression, Sharing Ideas and Opinions and Developing Critical Thinking. Descriptions of the teaching strategies are found in the appendix.

Providing Key Information

Students need information before they can move to higher-level thinking. This program uses a variety of strategies to provide the information students need to take actions for health. Strategies include:

- anonymous question box
- current events
- demonstrations
- experiments
- games and puzzles
- guest speakers
- information gathering
- interviewing
- oral presentations

Encouraging Creative Expression

Creative expression provides the opportunity to integrate language arts, fine arts and personal experience into learning. It also allows students the opportunity to demonstrate their understanding in ways that are unique to them. Creative expression encourages students to capitalize on their strengths and their interests. Strategies include:

- artistic expression
- creative writing
- dramatic presentations
- roleplays

PROGRAM OVERVIEW

TEACHING STRATEGIES

Sharing Ideas, Feelings and Opinions

In the sensitive area of health education, providing a safe atmosphere in which to discuss a variety of opinions and feelings is essential. Discussion provides the opportunity to clarify misinformation and correct misconceptions. Strategies include:

- brainstorming
- class discussion
- clustering
- continuum voting
- dyad discussion
- family discussion
- forced field analysis
- journal writing
- panel discussion
- self-assessment
- small groups
- surveys and inventories

Developing Critical Thinking

Critical thinking skills are crucial if students are to adopt healthy behaviors. Healthy choices necessitate the ability to become independent thinkers, analyze problems and devise solutions in real-life situations. Strategies include:

- case studies
- cooperative learning groups
- debates
- factual writing
- media analysis
- personal contracts
- research

PROGRAM OVERVIEW

SKILLS INFUSION

Studies of high-risk children and adolescents show that certain characteristics are common to children who succeed in adverse situations. These children are called resilient. Evaluation of educational programs designed to build resiliency has shown that several elements are important for success. The most important is the inclusion of activities designed to build personal and social skills.

Throughout each resource book, students practice skills along with the content addressed in the activities. Activities that naturally infuse personal and social skills are identified.

- **Communication**—Students with effective communication skills are able to express thoughts and feelings, actively listen to others, and give clear verbal and nonverbal messages related to health or any other aspect of their lives.

- **Decision Making**—Students with effective decision-making skills are able to identify decision points, gather information, and analyze and evaluate alternatives before they take action. This skill is important to promote positive health choices.

- **Assertiveness**—Students with effective assertiveness skills are able to resist pressure and influence from peers, advertising or others that may be in conflict with healthy behavior. This skill involves the ability to negotiate in stressful situations and refuse unwanted influences.

- **Stress Management**—Students with effective stress-management skills are able to cope with stress as a normal part of life. They are able to identify situations and conditions that produce stress and adopt healthy coping behaviors.

- **Goal Setting**—Students with effective goal-setting skills are able to clarify goals based on their needs and interests. They are able to set realistic goals, identify the sub-steps to goals, take action and evaluate their progress. They are able to learn from mistakes and change goals as needed.

PROGRAM OVERVIEW

WORKING WITH FAMILIES AND COMMUNITIES

A few general principles can help you be most effective in teaching about health:

- Establish a rapport with your students, their families and your community.
- Prepare yourself so that you are comfortable with the content and instructional process required to teach about fitness and health successfully.
- Be aware of state laws and guidelines established by your school district that relate to health.
- Invite parents and other family members to attend a preview of the materials.

Family involvement improves student learning. Encourage family members and other volunteers to help you in the classroom as you teach these activities.

THE COMMUNICATION AND SELF-ESTEEM RESOURCE BOOK

WHY TEACH ABOUT COMMUNICATION AND SELF-ESTEEM?

The way we communicate with others is important to health. Knowledge, attitudes and skills determine individual health behavior. How we feel about ourselves, or self-esteem, can also positively or negatively influence health choices.

High self-esteem is considered important in determining students' current and future success and happiness. The ability to communicate ideas, thoughts, feelings and beliefs is connected to enhanced self-esteem, decision making and problem solving. Effective communication is a lifelong and complex process. It affects relationships with family, friends, coworkers and community members.

Enhanced self-esteem increases student motivation and improves academic success. This resource book of activities will help students gain skills in communication and decision making, which can foster enhanced self-esteem.

Communication, Self-Esteem and High School Students

It is important for students to realize that self-esteem is a feeling and cannot be directly observed. It is often related to how we judge ourselves. It is related to self-confidence and to feelings of satisfaction. It is central to the ability to cope with the experiences and challenges of life. Thus, it is linked to health behavior choices.

Developmentally, high school students are striving for independence. They are faced with health behavior choices and challenges in their relationships that will affect their health and their lives. Their ability to communicate with others, make decisions and solve problems is central to overall health and happiness.

The motivations for health behaviors are explored in these units. The application of skills to real-life situations is also addressed. The units are designed to help students gain knowledge, develop positive attitudes about themselves and build skills that can be applied to everyday situations in their own lives.

Background Information About Communication and Self-Esteem

Instant Expert sections throughout this book give you all the information you need to teach each unit.

Influences on Health Behavior (p. 10)
Self-Esteem and Mental Health (p. 25)
Promoting Self-Esteem (p. 37)
Problem Solving and Decision Making (p. 51)
Types of Communication (p. 64)
Effective Communication (p. 80)

THE COMMUNICATION AND SELF-ESTEEM RESOURCE BOOK

OBJECTIVES

Students Will Be Able to:

Unit 1: Influences on Health Behavior

- Describe motivations for health behavior.
- Identify influences on health behavior.
- Explain factors involved in trying to change health behavior.

Unit 2: Who Am I?

- Explain the importance of self-esteem.
- Describe characteristics of people who exhibit high levels of mental health and self-actualization.

Unit 3: Promoting Positive Self-Esteem

- Describe personal actions that can improve self-esteem.

Unit 4: Step by Step

- Describe specific steps that can be used for problem solving and decision making.
- Demonstrate steps in problem solving and decision making.

Unit 5: Types of Communication

- Explain the different levels of communication.
- Demonstrate nonverbal communication.
- Describe ways to promote self-esteem by improving communication skills.

Unit 6: Promoting Communication

- Identify the components of successful communication.
- Demonstrate effective communication.

ANATOMY OF A UNIT

PREPARING TO TEACH

Objective identifies what students are expected to be able to do after instruction.

Getting Started lists preparation needed, including which masters to use.

Purpose states the rationale for the unit. **Main Points** are the key issues addressed. **Review** identifies the readings to increase your expertise in the content.

Vocabulary provides definitions of words used in the unit.

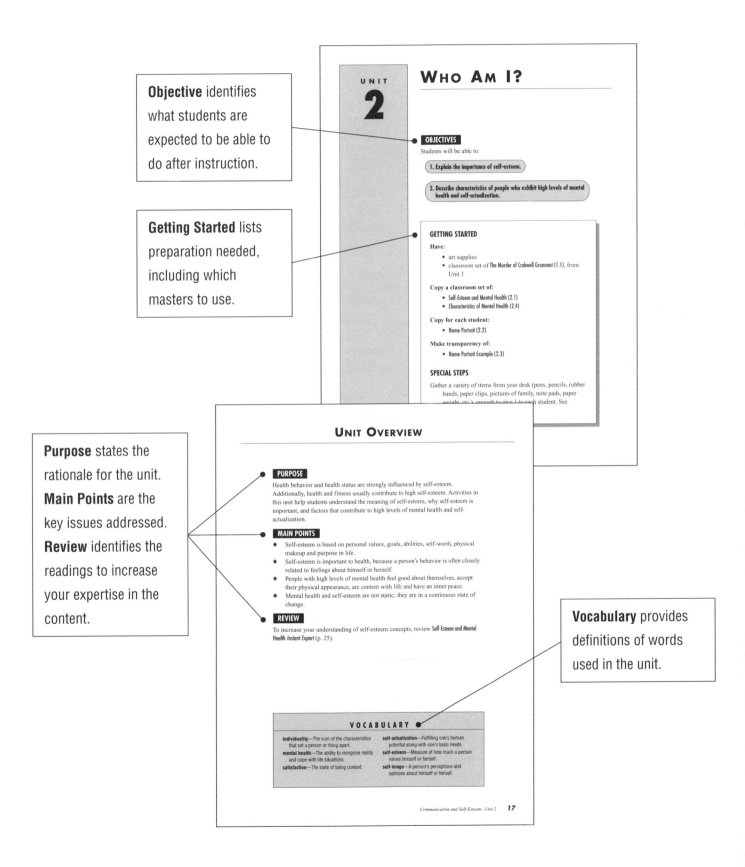

UNIT **2**

WHO AM I?

OBJECTIVES

Students will be able to:

1. Explain the importance of self-esteem.

2. Describe characteristics of people who exhibit high levels of mental health and self-actualization.

GETTING STARTED

Have:
- art supplies
- classroom set of *The Murder of Crabwell Grommet* (1.1), from Unit 1

Copy a classroom set of:
- *Self-Esteem and Mental Health* (2.1)
- *Characteristics of Mental Health* (2.4)

Copy for each student:
- *Name Portrait* (2.2)

Make transparency of:
- *Name Portrait Example* (2.3)

SPECIAL STEPS

Gather a variety of items from your desk (pens, pencils, rubber bands, paper clips, pictures of family, note pads, paper weight, etc.), enough to give 1 to each student. See

UNIT OVERVIEW

PURPOSE

Health behavior and health status are strongly influenced by self-esteem. Additionally, health and fitness usually contribute to high self-esteem. Activities in this unit help students understand the meaning of self-esteem, why self-esteem is important, and factors that contribute to high levels of mental health and self-actualization.

MAIN POINTS

* Self-esteem is based on personal values, goals, abilities, self-worth, physical makeup and purpose in life.
* Self-esteem is important to health, because a person's behavior is often closely related to feelings about himself or herself.
* People with high levels of mental health feel good about themselves, accept their physical appearance, are content with life and have an inner peace.
* Mental health and self-esteem are not static; they are in a continuous state of change.

REVIEW

To increase your understanding of self-esteem concepts, review *Self-Esteem and Mental Health Instant Expert* (p. 25).

VOCABULARY

individuality—The sum of the characteristics that set a person or thing apart.
mental health—The ability to recognize reality and cope with life situations.
satisfaction—The state of being content.

self-actualization—Fulfilling one's human potential along with one's basic needs.
self-esteem—Measure of how much a person values himself or herself.
self-image—A person's perceptions and opinions about himself or herself.

ANATOMY OF A UNIT

TEACHING THE ACTIVITIES

Instant Expert pages provide concise background information for you. They follow each unit.

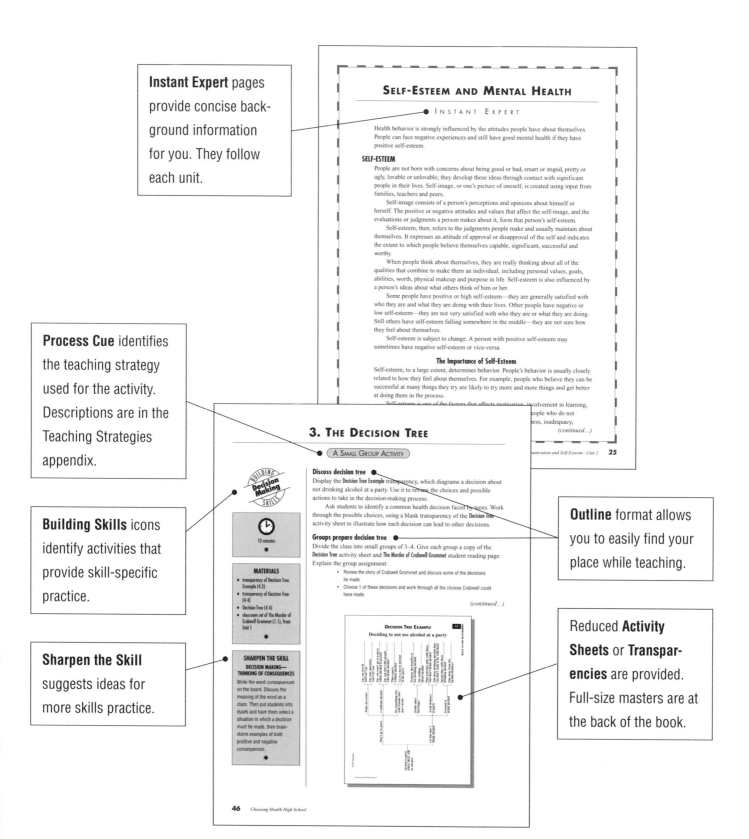

SELF-ESTEEM AND MENTAL HEALTH

INSTANT EXPERT

Health behavior is strongly influenced by the attitudes people have about themselves. People can face negative experiences and still have good mental health if they have positive self-esteem.

SELF-ESTEEM

People are not born with concerns about being good or bad, smart or stupid, pretty or ugly, lovable or unlovable; they develop these ideas through contact with significant people in their lives. Self-image, or one's picture of oneself, is created using input from families, teachers and peers.

Self-image consists of a person's perceptions and opinions about himself or herself. The positive or negative attitudes and values that affect the self-image, and the evaluations or judgments a person makes about it, form that person's self-esteem.

Self-esteem, then, refers to the judgments people make and usually maintain about themselves. It expresses an attitude of approval or disapproval of the self and indicates the extent to which people believe themselves capable, significant, successful and worthy.

When people think about themselves, they are really thinking about all of the qualities that combine to make them an individual, including personal values, goals, abilities, worth, physical makeup and purpose in life. Self-esteem is also influenced by a person's ideas about what others think of him or her.

Some people have positive or high self-esteem—they are generally satisfied with who they are and what they are doing with their lives. Other people have negative or low self-esteem—they are not very satisfied with who they are or what they are doing. Still others have self-esteem falling somewhere in the middle—they are not sure how they feel about themselves.

Self-esteem is subject to change. A person with positive self-esteem may sometimes have negative self-esteem or vice-versa.

The Importance of Self-Esteem

Self-esteem, to a large extent, determines behavior. People's behavior is usually closely related to how they feel about themselves. For example, people who believe they can be successful at many things they try are likely to try more and more things and get better at doing them in the process.

Self-esteem is one of the factors that affects motivation, involvement in learning, people who do not ess, inadequacy,

(continued...)

...munication and Self-Esteem—Unit 2 **25**

Process Cue identifies the teaching strategy used for the activity. Descriptions are in the Teaching Strategies appendix.

Building Skills icons identify activities that provide skill-specific practice.

Sharpen the Skill suggests ideas for more skills practice.

3. THE DECISION TREE

(A SMALL GROUP ACTIVITY)

BUILDING Decision Making **SKILLS**

🕐 10 minutes
✳

MATERIALS
- transparency of Decision Tree Example (4.3)
- transparency of Decision Tree (4.4)
- Decision Tree (4.4)
- classroom set of The Murder of Crabwell Grommet (1.1), from Unit 1
✳

SHARPEN THE SKILL
DECISION MAKING— THINKING OF CONSEQUENCES

Write the word *consequences* on the board. Discuss the meaning of the word as a class. Then put students into dyads and have them select a situation in which a decision must be made, then brainstorm examples of both positive and negative consequences.
✳

Discuss decision tree
Display the **Decision Tree Example** transparency, which diagrams a decision about not drinking alcohol at a party. Use it to review the choices and possible actions to take in the decision-making process.

Ask students to identify a common health decision faced by teens. Work through the possible choices, using a blank transparency of the **Decision Tree** activity sheet to illustrate how each decision can lead to other decisions.

Groups prepare decision tree
Divide the class into small groups of 3–4. Give each group a copy of the **Decision Tree** activity sheet and **The Murder of Crabwell Grommet** student reading page. Explain the group assignment:
- Review the story of Crabwell Grommet and discuss some of the decisions he made.
- Choose 1 of these decisions and work through all the choices Crabwell could have made.

(continued...)

DECISION TREE EXAMPLE
Deciding to not use alcohol at a party

Outline format allows you to easily find your place while teaching.

Reduced **Activity Sheets** or **Transparencies** are provided. Full-size masters are at the back of the book.

ANATOMY OF A UNIT

SPECIAL FEATURES

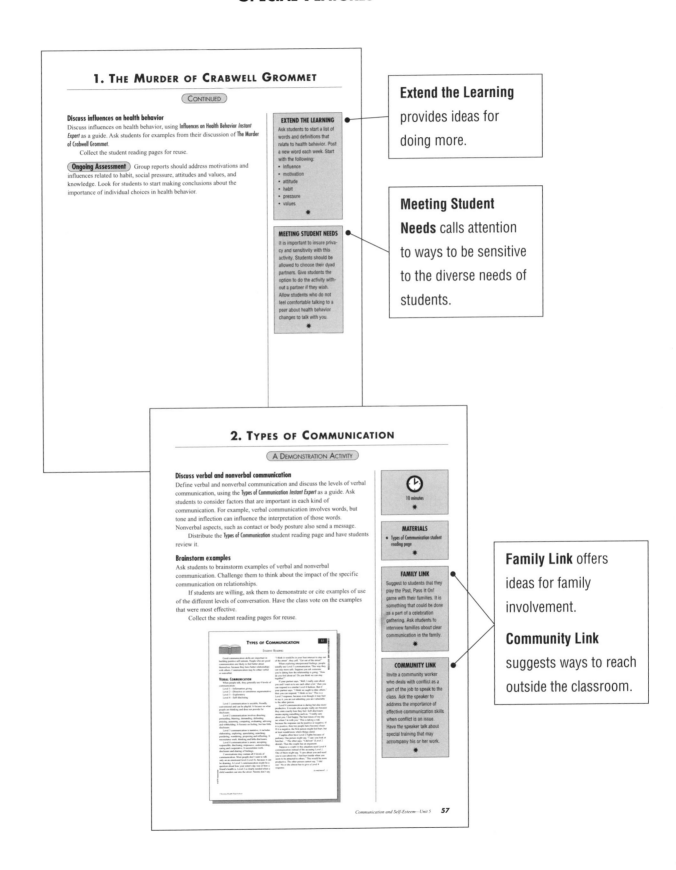

Extend the Learning provides ideas for doing more.

Meeting Student Needs calls attention to ways to be sensitive to the diverse needs of students.

Family Link offers ideas for family involvement.

Community Link suggests ways to reach outside the classroom.

ANATOMY OF A UNIT

EVALUATION FEATURES

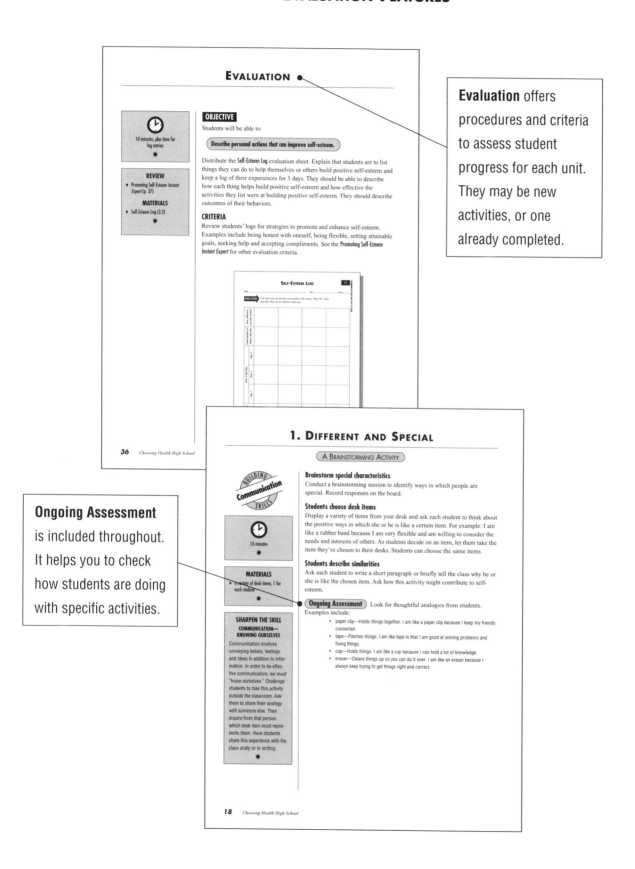

Evaluation offers procedures and criteria to assess student progress for each unit. They may be new activities, or one already completed.

EVALUATION

OBJECTIVE

Students will be able to:

Describe personal actions that can improve self-esteem.

Distribute the Self-Esteem Log evaluation sheet. Explain that students are to list things they can do to help themselves or others build positive self-esteem and keep a log of their experiences for 3 days. They should be able to describe how each thing helps build positive self-esteem and how effective the activities they list were at building positive self-esteem. They should describe outcomes of their behaviors.

CRITERIA

Review students' logs for strategies to promote and enhance self-esteem. Examples include being honest with oneself, being flexible, setting attainable goals, seeking help and accepting compliments. See the Promoting Self-Esteem *Instant Expert* for other evaluation criteria.

10 minutes, plus time for log entries

REVIEW
- Promoting Self-Esteem *Instant Expert* (p. 37)

MATERIALS
- Self-Esteem Log (3.2)

SELF-ESTEEM LOG

36   *Choosing Health High School*

Ongoing Assessment is included throughout. It helps you to check how students are doing with specific activities.

1. DIFFERENT AND SPECIAL

A BRAINSTORMING ACTIVITY

Brainstorm special characteristics
Conduct a brainstorming session to identify ways in which people are special. Record responses on the board.

Students choose desk items
Display a variety of items from your desk and ask each student to think about the positive ways in which she or he is like a certain item. For example: I am like a rubber band because I am very flexible and am willing to consider the needs and interests of others. As students decide on an item, let them take the item they've chosen to their desks. Students can choose the same items.

Students describe similarities
Ask each student to write a short paragraph or briefly tell the class why he or she is like the chosen item. Ask how this activity might contribute to self-esteem.

Ongoing Assessment Look for thoughtful analogies from students. Examples include:
- paper clip—Holds things together. I am like a paper clip because I keep my friends connected.
- tape—Patches things. I am like tape in that I am good at solving problems and fixing things.
- cup—Holds things. I am like a cup because I can hold a lot of knowledge.
- eraser—Cleans things up so you can do it over. I am like an eraser because I always keep trying to get things right and correct.

10 minutes

MATERIALS
- a variety of desk items, 1 for each student

SHARPEN THE SKILL
COMMUNICATION—KNOWING OURSELVES
Communication involves conveying beliefs, feelings and ideas in addition to information. In order to be effective communicators, we must "know ourselves." Challenge students to take this activity outside the classroom. Ask them to share their analogy with someone else. Then inquire from that person which desk item most represents them. Have students share this experience with the class orally or in writing.

18   *Choosing Health High School*

INFLUENCES ON HEALTH BEHAVIOR

TIME

2 periods

ACTIVITIES

1. The Murder of Crabwell Grommet

2. Influences on Health Behavior

3. Changing Health Habits

INFLUENCES ON HEALTH BEHAVIOR

OBJECTIVES

Students will be able to:

1. Describe motivations for health behavior.

2. Identify influences on health behavior.

3. Explain factors involved in trying to change health behavior.

GETTING STARTED

Copy a classroom set of:

- The Murder of Crabwell Grommet (1.1)

Copy for each student:

- Health Habit to Change (1.2)

Make transparency of:

- Health Habit to Change Example (1.3)

UNIT OVERVIEW

PURPOSE

Health behavior, which is influenced by knowledge, attitudes and skills, is one of the keys to enhancing health status. This unit helps students understand motivations for health behavior, including cultural influences, and ways to change health behavior.

MAIN POINTS

* The 4 motivations that underlie most health behavior are social pressure, habits, attitudes and values, and knowledge.
* Health behavior decisions are strongly influenced by perceptions of the extent to which family, friends and associates engage in particular health behaviors.
* Some health behaviors can become habits, and the original reasons for doing them and their health effects may be forgotten.
* Knowledge can influence some health behaviors, but it does not guarantee that certain behaviors will occur.
* Cultural, personal and religious beliefs and practices can influence health behavior.
* Behavior change involves resisting social influences, finding alternative ways of obtaining reinforcement, and applying certain high-level skills.
* Individual health choices have the greatest influence on health.

REVIEW

To increase your understanding of influences on health behavior, review Influences on Health Behavior *Instant Expert* (p. 10).

VOCABULARY

attitude—State of mind or opinion.

culture—Collection of shared practices, rules and values of a group.

habit—An act that is done often, in a certain way, and has become automatic.

health—Well-being in all dimensions of life including mental, emotional, social and physical.

influence—The ability of a person or thing to affect others.

1. THE MURDER OF CRABWELL GROMMET

50 minutes

MATERIALS

♦ classroom set of The Murder of Crabwell Grommet (1.1)

Students read story

Distribute **The Murder of Crabwell Grommet** student reading page and have students read it individually or as a class.

Groups discuss story

Divide the class into cooperative learning groups of 3–4. Explain the group assignment:

- Assign a responsibility to each member—readers, recorder, reporter.
- Discuss the following questions:
  - What factors influenced the health of Crabwell Grommet?
  - What control did Crabwell have over those factors?
  - What could Crabwell have done differently regarding his health?
  - Why did Crabwell's widow think he died of natural causes?

Groups report

Ask groups to report their responses to the questions. Discuss group responses.

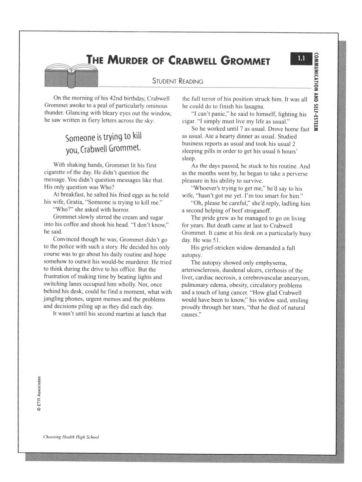

THE MURDER OF CRABWELL GROMMET 1.1

STUDENT READING

On the morning of his 42nd birthday, Crabwell Grommet awoke to a peal of particularly ominous thunder. Glancing with bleary eyes out the window, he saw written in fiery letters across the sky:

Someone is trying to kill you, Crabwell Grommet.

With shaking hands, Grommet lit his first cigarette of the day. He didn't question the message. You didn't question messages like that. His only question was Who?

At breakfast, he salted his fried eggs as he told his wife, Gratia, "Someone is trying to kill me."

"Who?" she asked with horror.

Grommet slowly stirred the cream and sugar into his coffee and shook his head. "I don't know," he said.

Convinced though he was, Grommet didn't go to the police with such a story. He decided his only course was to go about his daily routine and hope somehow to outwit his would-be murderer. He tried to think during the drive to his office. But the frustration of making time by beating lights and switching lanes occupied him wholly. Nor, once behind his desk, could he find a moment, what with jangling phones, urgent memos and the problems and decisions piling up as they did each day.

It wasn't until his second martini at lunch that

the full terror of his position struck him. It was all he could do to finish his lasagna.

"I can't panic," he said to himself, lighting his cigar. "I simply must live my life as usual."

So he worked until 7 as usual. Drove home fast as usual. Ate a hearty dinner as usual. Studied business reports as usual and took his usual 2 sleeping pills in order to get his usual 6 hours' sleep.

As the days passed, he stuck to his routine. And as the months went by, he began to take a perverse pleasure in his ability to survive.

"Whoever's trying to get me," he'd say to his wife, "hasn't got me yet. I'm too smart for him."

"Oh, please be careful," she'd reply, ladling him a second helping of beef stroganoff.

The pride grew as he managed to go on living for years. But death came at last to Crabwell Grommet. It came at his desk on a particularly busy day. He was 51.

His grief-stricken widow demanded a full autopsy.

The autopsy showed only emphysema, arteriosclerosis, duodenal ulcers, cirrhosis of the liver, cardiac necrosis, a cerebrovascular aneurysm, pulmonary edema, obesity, circulatory problems and a touch of lung cancer. "How glad Crabwell would have been to know," his widow said, smiling proudly through her tears, "that he died of natural causes."

COMMUNICATION AND SELF-ESTEEM

© ETR Associates

Choosing Health High School

---

1. THE MURDER OF CRABWELL GROMMET

Discuss influences on health behavior

Discuss influences on health behavior, using Influences on Health Behavior *Instant Expert* as a guide. Ask students for examples from their discussion of The Murder of Crabwell Grommet.

Collect the student reading pages for reuse.

Ongoing Assessment Group reports should address motivations and influences related to habit, social pressure, attitudes and values, and knowledge. Look for students to start making conclusions about the importance of individual choices in health behavior.

EXTEND THE LEARNING

Ask students to start a list of words and definitions that relate to health behavior. Post a new word each week. Start with the following:

- influence
- motivation
- attitude
- habit
- pressure
- values

2. INFLUENCES ON HEALTH BEHAVIOR

20 minutes

Groups list influences

Divide the class into groups of 3–4, or have them remain in their groups from Activity 1. Explain the group assignment:

- List ways that teens influence each other in the following categories: social pressures, habits, attitudes and values, and knowledge.
- Identify which of the listed influences are positive influences and which are negative influences.
- Be prepared to report to the class.

Groups report

Have groups report the influences they listed and whether these influences are positive or negative.

3. CHANGING HEALTH HABITS

Brainstorm health habits

Conduct a discussion to clarify the meaning of *health habits*. Brainstorm possible health habits students may be interested in changing. Write the list on the board.

Students choose habits to change

Ask students to think about a health habit they would like to change. Distribute the **Health Habit to Change** activity sheet and explain how to complete it using the **Health Habit to Change Example** transparency.

Have students write down the habit they would like to change and answer the questions on the activity sheet.

Dyads discuss assignment

Allow students to choose a partner. Ask pairs to discuss the activity sheet and assist each other. Ask for volunteers to share some of their answers. Be sure that example answers to all questions are given.

20 minutes

MATERIALS

◆ Health Habit to Change (1.2)
◆ transparency of Health Habit to Change Example (1.3)

MEETING STUDENT NEEDS

It is important to insure privacy and sensitivity with this activity. Students should be allowed to choose their dyad partners. Give students the option to do the activity without a partner if they wish. Allow students who do not feel comfortable talking to a peer about health behavior changes to talk with you.

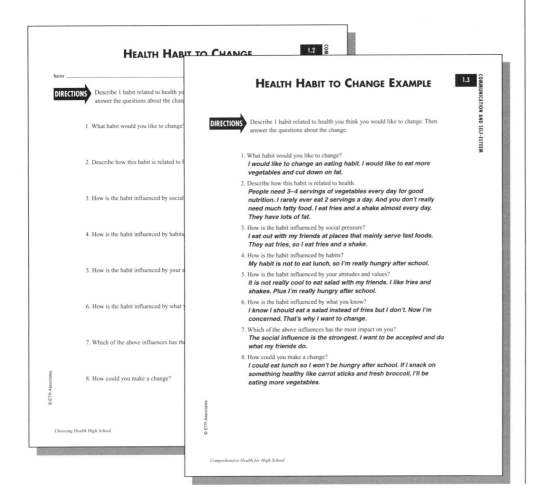

EVALUATION

REVIEW

♦ Influences on Health Behavior
  Instant Expert (p. 10)

OBJECTIVE 1

Students will be able to:

> **Describe motivations for health behavior.**

Assess student responses during the discussion and group reports about Crabwell Grommet's health behavior in Activity 1. Ask students to summarize Crabwell's motivations for health behavior either orally or in writing.

CRITERIA

Look for students to describe motivations related to social pressure, habits, attitudes and values, and knowledge. See the **Influences on Health Behavior** *Instant Expert* for specific examples of these motivations.

OBJECTIVE 2

Students will be able to:

> **Identify influences on health behavior.**

Observe student comments on ways that teens influence each other in Activity 2 to determine their understanding of positive and negative influences on health behavior.

CRITERIA

Look for comments to demonstrate an understanding of the depth of influence that social pressure in particular has on teens' health-related choices. Also look for students to draw conclusions about the importance of individual choices about health behavior.

(continued...)

EVALUATION

OBJECTIVE 3

Students will be able to:

> **Explain factors involved in trying to change health behavior.**

Ask students to explain general factors that might influence them or others who are trying to change health behavior(s). Tell them to provide examples and details in their explanations. This can be done orally or in writing.

CRITERIA

Look for students to provide examples of factors, including motivation, cost, access, needed skills, values, other people and social support. See the **Influences on Health Behavior** *Instant Expert* for evaluation criteria.

10 minutes

REVIEW

♦ Influences on Health Behavior
  Instant Expert (p. 10)

INFLUENCES ON HEALTH BEHAVIOR

Health behavior—the way they take care of themselves physically, emotionally and socially—influences how people think, feel and act. The promotion of healthy behavior requires health knowledge, positive attitudes, and skills that can be applied to everyday situations.

Health behaviors are influenced by many factors. When people feel well, they are not as concerned about changing health behaviors to promote health. Sometimes, people may delay seeking medical attention because they suspect their symptoms are a sign of something quite serious. Fear about health can also prevent people from acquiring the information needed to make sound decisions and from facing health problems in a rational and constructive way.

MOTIVATIONS FOR HEALTH BEHAVIOR

Humans are social animals and are influenced by the ideas, feelings and actions of those around them. Motivation provides the impetus to act. As complicated as motivation for health behavior can be, 4 main motivations underlie most health behavior:

- social pressure
- habits
- attitudes and values
- knowledge

Social Pressure

Social pressure is the desire or belief that one needs to go along with or rebel against others' actions or expectations. Actions taken to look more masculine or feminine, to gain praise or avoid embarrassment, or to appear more mature are all motivated by social pressure. Because people are social animals, their thoughts and actions are heavily influenced by the opinions and actions of others, particularly those of peers, or social equals.

Many people act quite differently in a group than they do when alone. People who might not take certain risks on their own often do so in a group to gain peer acceptance. Many high school students, for example, will disobey school authorities in the "safety" of a group, but will heed those same authorities individually.

People's health behaviors are strongly influenced by their perceptions of the extent to which family, friends and associates engage in a particular type of health behavior (that is, its social acceptability). Peer and family influence can be an important tool in promoting health. One good example of how social pressure has changed attitudes and

(continued...)

INFLUENCES ON HEALTH BEHAVIOR

behavior is drinking and driving. Alcohol-related fatalities used to be thought of as "accidents." Today they are recognized as preventable events, and penalties for driving under the influence of alcohol or other drugs can be severe.

Habits

Behaviors that affect health often result from health habits, habits that may start because of some social or parental pressure. Most children, for example, begin to brush their teeth nightly because their parents insist they do it. Some begin to smoke because they desire acceptance from a family member or friend who smokes.

The more an act is repeated, the easier it becomes, and the more comfortable and self-assured one feels in doing it. Soon the act passes into an unthinking routine, or habit. As habits become increasingly ingrained, one may forget both the original reasons for doing them and their potential effects on health. Bad habits may lead to people deliberately ignoring possible dangers.

Attitudes and Values

Attitudes and values influence health behavior in many ways. People may engage in some practices, such as running, reading or eating sweets, purely for pleasure. These activities may have beneficial, harmful or no real consequences for health.

People may engage in or avoid other behaviors because of personal or religious values. On principle, one may choose to become a vegetarian or to not smoke, drink or engage in premarital sexual activity.

Knowledge

Although people may not always act as reasonably as they could, they are not simply the victims of emotions, habits and environmental influences. People take or avoid some actions mainly because they are aware of health benefits and risks—they have knowledge. For example, they may eat certain foods, refuse to ride with a drunk driver and get periodic physical checkups.

Because people are most at ease when what they know is consistent with their attitudes and values, they sometimes seek out information that will support personal attitudes while ignoring information that doesn't. This tendency takes a considerable effort to overcome.

Many people once assumed that if teachers simply poured out knowledge, thirsty students would drink it up to improve their lives. This has become known as the "fallacy of the empty vessel"—knowledge alone is seldom sufficient reason to change.

(continued...)

INFLUENCES ON HEALTH BEHAVIOR

People find many reasons to ignore information. They may respond to knowledge only when it becomes very important to them. For example, some people do not pay any attention to salt intake until they have developed high blood pressure. This discrepancy between personal health behavior and general health knowledge is one of the most publicized dilemmas related to health today.

CULTURAL INFLUENCES ON HEALTH

Though people may feel that these 4 motivating forces—social pressure, habits, attitudes and values, and knowledge—are unique to themselves, they usually share them with many others. Beliefs and practices are often linked to a larger social context. A personal value we believe in strongly is usually a product of what we have been taught by others. If our teachers from infancy had been radically different, our values would probably be different as well.

The collection of shared habitual practices, behavioral rules, and values and beliefs of a group of people constitutes its culture. People in the United States, for example, are generally assumed to speak English, believe in majority political rule and religious tolerance, and drive on the right side of the road. These are shared aspects of their culture.

Smaller groups within society—such as Chinese Americans, Irish Americans and high school students (teenage subculture)—may have distinct practices that set them apart from other groups, even though they share society's major cultural values. Each of these groups is called a subculture.

Cultural and subcultural practices can influence health. For example, fried foods traditionally form part of the diet in certain subcultures. Because this diet results in a high intake of cholesterol, these groups have a greater incidence of illnesses related to high cholesterol than other groups.

The influence of cultural practices on health is sometimes overlooked. For example, within the teenage subculture, the need to eat food with friends can result in the intake of unnecessary calories; the need to have a car to reach certain destinations can result in a lack of physical activity, both of which contribute to health problems.

(continued...)

INFLUENCES ON HEALTH BEHAVIOR

INTERACTIONS AMONG INFLUENCES

The determinants of health behavior can be remarkably complex. Biological, psychological and sociocultural factors, as well as the interplay among them, must be understood. Consider the example of smoking to examine how determinants interact.

At the physiological level, nicotine produces powerful and varied effects. These effects interact with other forces, particularly the fact that smoking is a strong habit and very difficult to change. It becomes conditioned and automatic.

Social and cultural factors also play a part. Role models of peers and others, social support or lack of support, and the personal and cultural meaning of smoking all have an impact. If one is trying to change a behavior such as smoking, comprehensive behavior-change strategies are needed. An approach that takes into account the important functions smoking serves and is tailored to the individual will be most successful.

SKILLS FOR BEHAVIOR CHANGE

Certain skills are important if behavior change is desired. These include resisting social influences, finding alternative ways of obtaining reinforcement, and high-level skills such as knowing how to choose and prepare nutritious snacks or how to do breast self-examination.

People can change cultural norms to improve the quality of their lives; however, norms are easy to describe and difficult to change. The best way to begin is to associate with others who share enthusiasm for positive health behaviors, such as vigorous physical activity. We can also encourage and support those who are attempting to make positive changes in their lifestyles. Just as culture plays an important role in development, people can play an important role in the creation of cultural norms. For example, in recent years people have heavily influenced norms related to smoking. It is now far less acceptable to smoke in public places than it was just a few years ago.

In the final analysis, individuals have the greatest influence on their own destinies. They can choose to become aware of the many influences on their health, to alter these influences when possible and appropriate, and to arrive at a balance conducive to optimum health.

UNIT 2

WHO AM I?

TIME
2 periods

ACTIVITIES
1. Different and Special
2. Facts About Mental Health
3. Name Portraits
4. Characteristics of Mental Health
5. The Self-Esteem of Crabwell Grommet

WHO AM I?

OBJECTIVES

Students will be able to:

1. Explain the importance of self-esteem.

2. Describe characteristics of people who exhibit high levels of mental health and self-actualization.

GETTING STARTED

Have:

- art supplies
- classroom set of The Murder of Crabwell Grommet (1.1), from Unit 1

Copy a classroom set of:

- Self-Esteem and Mental Health (2.1)
- Characteristics of Mental Health (2.4)

Copy for each student:

- Name Portrait (2.2)

Make transparency of:

- Name Portrait Example (2.3)

SPECIAL STEPS

Gather a variety of items from your desk (pens, pencils, rubber bands, paper clips, pictures of family, note pads, paperweight, etc.), enough to give 1 to each student. See Activity 1 (p. 18).

UNIT OVERVIEW

PURPOSE

Health behavior and health status are strongly influenced by self-esteem. Additionally, health and fitness usually contribute to high self-esteem. Activities in this unit help students understand the meaning of self-esteem, why self-esteem is important, and factors that contribute to high levels of mental health and self-actualization.

MAIN POINTS

* Self-esteem is based on personal values, goals, abilities, self-worth, physical makeup and purpose in life.
* Self-esteem is important to health, because a person's behavior is often closely related to feelings about himself or herself.
* People with high levels of mental health feel good about themselves, accept their physical appearance, are content with life and have an inner peace.
* Mental health and self-esteem are not static; they are in a continuous state of change.

REVIEW

To increase your understanding of self-esteem concepts, review Self-Esteem and Mental Health *Instant Expert* (p. 25).

VOCABULARY

individuality—The sum of the characteristics that set a person or thing apart.

mental health—The ability to recognize reality and cope with life situations.

satisfaction—The state of being content.

self-actualization—Fulfilling one's human potential along with one's basic needs.

self-esteem—Measure of how much a person values himself or herself.

self-image—A person's perceptions and opinions about himself or herself.

1. DIFFERENT AND SPECIAL

10 minutes

MATERIALS

♦ a variety of desk items, 1 for each student

❋

SHARPEN THE SKILL

COMMUNICATION—KNOWING OURSELVES

Communication involves conveying beliefs, feelings and ideas in addition to information. In order to be effective communicators, we must "know ourselves." Challenge students to take this activity outside the classroom. Ask them to share their analogy with someone else. Then inquire from that person which desk item most represents them. Have students share this experience with the class orally or in writing.

Brainstorm special characteristics

Conduct a brainstorming session to identify ways in which people are special. Record responses on the board.

Students choose desk items

Display a variety of items from your desk and ask each student to think about the positive ways in which she or he is like a certain item. For example: I am like a rubber band because I am very flexible and am willing to consider the needs and interests of others. As students decide on an item, let them take the item they've chosen to their desks. Students can choose the same items.

Students describe similarities

Ask each student to write a short paragraph or briefly tell the class why he or she is like the chosen item. Ask how this activity might contribute to self-esteem.

Ongoing Assessment Look for thoughtful analogies from students. Examples include:

- paper clip—Holds things together. I am like a paper clip because I keep my friends connected.
- tape—Patches things. I am like tape in that I am good at solving problems and fixing things.
- cup—Holds things. I am like a cup because I can hold a lot of knowledge.
- eraser—Cleans things up so you can do it over. I am like an eraser because I always keep trying to get things right and correct.

2. FACTS ABOUT MENTAL HEALTH

Students read about mental health

Distribute a copy of the Self-Esteem and Mental Health student reading page. Give students 5 minutes to read the information.

List facts

Ask students to identify facts about mental health. Make a list of the facts on the board as students identify them.

Discuss importance

After a long list of facts has been recorded, challenge students to identify the 5 most important facts. Tell them to be prepared to defend their decisions about the top 5.

Collect the student reading pages for reuse.

10 minutes

✳

MATERIALS

◆ classroom set of Self-Esteem and Mental Health (2.1)

✳

SELF-ESTEEM AND MENTAL HEALTH [2.1]

STUDENT READING

SELF-ESTEEM

People are not born with an idea that they are good or bad, smart or stupid, pretty or ugly, lovable or unlovable. They develop these ideas through contact with significant people in their lives. Our self-image or picture of ourselves, is based on input from families, teachers and peers.

Self-image is what a person perceives and believes about himself or herself. The attitudes and values that affect self-image, and the judgments a person makes about it, form that person's self-esteem. Self-esteem indicates how capable, significant, successful and worthy people believe themselves to be.

When people think about themselves, they are really thinking about all of the qualities that make them an individual, including personal values, goals, abilities, worth, physical appearance and purpose in life. Self-esteem is also influenced by what people believe others think of them.

Some people have positive or high self-esteem. They are generally satisfied with who they are and what they are doing with their lives. Other people have negative or low self-esteem. They are not very satisfied with who they are or what they are doing. Some people's self-esteem falls somewhere in between. They may not be sure how they feel about themselves.

Self-esteem can change. A person with positive self-esteem may sometimes have negative self-esteem or vice-versa.

WHY IS SELF-ESTEEM IMPORTANT?

Self-esteem has a large effect on people's behavior. Behavior is usually linked to how people feel about themselves. For example, if you believe you can be successful at many things you try, chances are you will try more and more things—and get better at doing them.

Positive self-esteem helps increase motivation and encourages learning. It helps people succeed in their relationships and careers. People who do not have positive self-esteem may feel unworthy,

inadequate, helpless, inferior, or that they can't improve their lives. People with negative self-esteem often feel they will fail.

MENTAL HEALTH

Mental health measures how well a person is able to cope with life's events, grow emotionally, and develop to the fullest potential. Positive mental health means feeling good about yourself. This includes accepting how you look, being content with life, and having inner peace. It also means a person actively seeks new experiences and challenges.

People with positive mental health enjoy many different interests and activities. They tend to use good judgment and think clearly. They are self-disciplined in their thinking and actions. They like other people. Like everyone else, they have problems. But they know that coping with problems is part of life.

People with poor mental health are more likely to have conflicting feelings about their lives. They often don't think ahead or follow through on things. They may do things to discourage friendships or good relations with others (such as provoking people). They may not even be aware they are doing this. They may find it hard to see beyond their own wants and needs.

SELF-ACTUALIZATION

Self-actualization is a term that means a person has positive self-esteem and mental health. People who are self-actualized have come to terms with their own place in the world. They seem to have a purpose outside themselves or be involved in a cause they really care about. They are comfortable with themselves and their lives. A self-actualized person has reached a very high level of mental health.

Being self-actualized means taking responsibility for looking at yourself and being honest. It demands awareness. It means you move toward realizing your full potential.

Choosing Health High School

3. NAME PORTRAITS

20 minutes

MATERIALS

♦ Name Portrait (2.2)
♦ transparency of Name Portrait Example (2.3)
♦ art supplies

MEETING STUDENT NEEDS

Students should be told that they are not required to share their work with the entire class. Only those who wish to share should be asked to do so.

Discuss name portraits

Distribute the Name Portrait activity sheet and display the Name Portrait Example transparency. Explain how to create a name portrait.

Students make and discuss portraits

Give students several minutes to fill out and decorate their own name portraits. Then discuss. Ask students:

- How did you feel while doing your name portrait?
- What does a name portrait have to do with self-esteem?

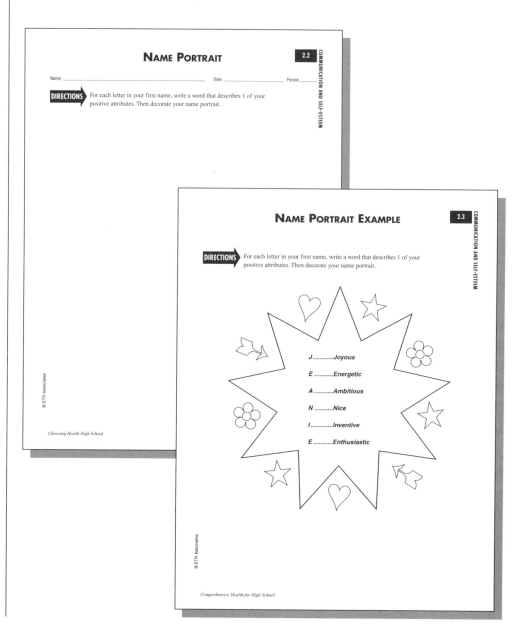

NAME PORTRAIT | 2.2 | COMMUNICATION AND SELF-ESTEEM

Name _____ Date _____ Period _____

DIRECTIONS For each letter in your first name, write a word that describes 1 of your positive attributes. Then decorate your name portrait.

© ETR Associates

Choosing Health High School

NAME PORTRAIT EXAMPLE | 2.3 | COMMUNICATION AND SELF-ESTEEM

DIRECTIONS For each letter in your first name, write a word that describes 1 of your positive attributes. Then decorate your name portrait.

J............Joyous
E ....Energetic
A ....Ambitious
N ....Nice
I...............Inventive
E ....Enthusiastic

© ETR Associates

Comprehensive Health for High School

4. CHARACTERISTICS OF MENTAL HEALTH

A SMALL GROUP ACTIVITY

Students read about mental health

Distribute the **Characteristics of Mental Health** student reading page and ask students to read it individually or as a class.

Discuss examples

Ask students for real-life examples of the mental health characteristics.

Groups list characteristics

Divide the class into small groups of 3–5. Explain the group assignment:

- Develop a list of characteristics of good mental health that are specific to teens.
- Compile characteristics of a teen who is self-actualized (comfortable with self and life, fulfilling potential) and discuss the difficulties in attaining this.
- Be prepared to report your lists to the class.

(continued...)

25 minutes

MATERIALS

- classroom set of Characteristics of Mental Health (2.4)

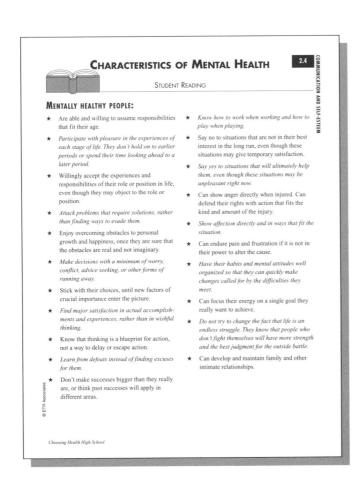

4. CHARACTERISTICS OF MENTAL HEALTH

SHARPEN THE SKILL

**STRESS MANAGEMENT—
MENTAL HEALTH AND
COPING SKILLS**

Mentally healthy people can effectively cope with stressors in life. Review the characteristics of mental health and identify those that are related to effective coping skills.

Groups report

Have each group share its lists with the class. Discuss similarities and differences between the lists. Did groups list characteristics that weren't included in the student reading?

Collect the student reading pages for reuse.

Ongoing Assessment Assess students' real-life examples of mental health characteristics and groups' lists of the characteristics of a self-actualized teen for their understanding of the concept of mental health and self-actualization. See the Characteristics of Mentally Healthy People and Self-Actualization sections of the **Self-Esteem and Mental Health** *Instant Expert* for assessment criteria.

5. The Self-Esteem of Crabwell Grommet

Groups discuss self-esteem

Keep students in their small groups from Activity 4. Distribute **The Murder of Crabwell Grommet** student reading page from Unit 1 and explain the group assignment:

- Review the reading.
- Discuss the following questions:
  - How would you evaluate Crabwell's self-esteem? What evidence would support your opinion?
  - List examples of ways that Crabwell's self-esteem changed throughout the story. What reasons can you think of for the changes?
  - What are examples of ways that a student's self-esteem might change in a day? in a week?
  - Be prepared to share your responses with the class.

Groups report

Have groups report on their discussions. Collect the student reading pages for reuse.

25 minutes

MATERIALS

- The Murder of Crabwell Grommet (1.1), from Unit 1

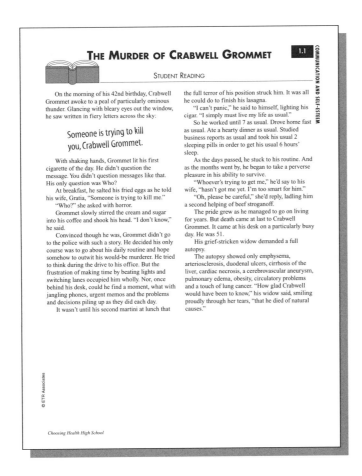

THE MURDER OF CRABWELL GROMMET 1.1

STUDENT READING

On the morning of his 42nd birthday, Crabwell Grommet awoke to a peal of particularly ominous thunder. Glancing with bleary eyes out the window, he saw written in fiery letters across the sky:

Someone is trying to kill you, Crabwell Grommet.

With shaking hands, Grommet lit his first cigarette of the day. He didn't question the message. You didn't question messages like that. His only question was Who?

At breakfast, he salted his fried eggs as he told his wife, Gratia, "Someone is trying to kill me."

"Who?" she asked with horror.

Grommet slowly stirred the cream and sugar into his coffee and shook his head. "I don't know," he said.

Convinced though he was, Grommet didn't go to the police with such a story. He decided his only course was to go about his daily routine and hope somehow to outwit his would-be murderer. He tried to think during the drive to his office. But the frustration of making time by beating lights and switching lanes occupied him wholly. Nor, once behind his desk, could he find a moment, what with jangling phones, urgent memos and the problems and decisions piling up as they did each day.

It wasn't until his second martini at lunch that the full terror of his position struck him. It was all he could do to finish his lasagna.

"I can't panic," he said to himself, lighting his cigar. "I simply must live my life as usual."

So he worked until 7 as usual. Drove home fast as usual. Ate a hearty dinner as usual. Studied business reports as usual and took his usual 2 sleeping pills in order to get his usual 6 hours' sleep.

As the days passed, he stuck to his routine. And as the months went by, he began to take a perverse pleasure in his ability to survive.

"Whoever's trying to get me," he'd say to his wife, "hasn't got me yet. I'm too smart for him."

"Oh, please be careful," she'd reply, ladling him a second helping of beef stroganoff.

The pride grew as he managed to go on living for years. But death came at last to Crabwell Grommet. It came at his desk on a particularly busy day. He was 51.

His grief-stricken widow demanded a full autopsy.

The autopsy showed only emphysema, arteriosclerosis, duodenal ulcers, cirrhosis of the liver, cardiac necrosis, a cerebrovascular aneurysm, pulmonary edema, obesity, circulatory problems and a touch of lung cancer. "How glad Crabwell would have been to know," his widow said, smiling proudly through her tears, "that he died of natural causes."

COMMUNICATION AND SELF-ESTEEM

© ETR Associates

Choosing Health High School

EVALUATION

10–30 minutes

✳

REVIEW

♦ Self-Esteem and Mental Health *Instant Expert* (p. 25)

✳

OBJECTIVE 1

Students will be able to:

> **Explain the importance of self-esteem.**

Ask students to list reasons why self-esteem is important. Encourage the use of multiple intelligences. Students can write a list, draw pictures, act out examples, create a map to self-esteem or use any other reasonable means to demonstrate their understanding.

CRITERIA

Look for students to demonstrate that self-esteem influences health behavior, helps motivate people to learn, helps promote success in life, and helps people meet challenges, try new things and generally feel good about themselves.

OBJECTIVE 2

Students will be able to:

> **Describe characteristics of people who exhibit high levels of mental health and self-actualization.**

Assess students' responses in class discussion and in the group work in Activity 4 for their ability to grasp the major concepts of mental health.

CRITERIA

See the Characteristics of Mental Health section of the **Self-Esteem and Mental Health** *Instant Expert* for evaluation criteria.

SELF-ESTEEM AND MENTAL HEALTH

Health behavior is strongly influenced by the attitudes people have about themselves. People can face negative experiences and still have good mental health if they have positive self-esteem.

SELF-ESTEEM

People are not born with concerns about being good or bad, smart or stupid, pretty or ugly, lovable or unlovable; they develop these ideas through contact with significant people in their lives. Self-image, or one's picture of oneself, is created using input from families, teachers and peers.

Self-image consists of a person's perceptions and opinions about himself or herself. The positive or negative attitudes and values that affect the self-image, and the evaluations or judgments a person makes about it, form that person's self-esteem.

Self-esteem, then, refers to the judgments people make and usually maintain about themselves. It expresses an attitude of approval or disapproval of the self and indicates the extent to which people believe themselves capable, significant, successful and worthy.

When people think about themselves, they are really thinking about all of the qualities that combine to make them an individual, including personal values, goals, abilities, worth, physical makeup and purpose in life. Self-esteem is also influenced by a person's ideas about what others think of him or her.

Some people have positive or high self-esteem—they are generally satisfied with who they are and what they are doing with their lives. Other people have negative or low self-esteem—they are not very satisfied with who they are or what they are doing. Still others have self-esteem falling somewhere in the middle—they are not sure how they feel about themselves.

Self-esteem is subject to change. A person with positive self-esteem may sometimes have negative self-esteem or vice-versa.

The Importance of Self-Esteem

Self-esteem, to a large extent, determines behavior. People's behavior is usually closely related to how they feel about themselves. For example, people who believe they can be successful at many things they try are likely to try more and more things and get better at doing them in the process.

Self-esteem is one of the factors that affects motivation, involvement in learning, and successful performance in relationships and occupations. People who do not have positive self-esteem may suffer from feelings of unworthiness, inadequacy,

(continued...)

SELF-ESTEEM AND MENTAL HEALTH

helplessness, inferiority, and a sense of being unable to improve their situation. Unlike the person who believes he or she can be successful, those without positive self-esteem often feel they will fail.

MENTAL HEALTH

Mental health is a measure of the capacity to cope with life situations, grow emotionally through them, develop to one's fullest potential, and grow in awareness and consciousness. Positive mental health includes feeling good about oneself, accepting physical appearance, being content with life, and gaining inner peace. It also includes active seeking of experiences that promote peak mental states.

People with good mental health are strongly motivated to build lives that promote self-actualization. They are diversified in their interests and activities and tend to use good judgment and think clearly. They are self-disciplined in their thinking and actions, and they like and seek out other people. They may have problems, but they know that coping with problems is part of life and believe in their ability to solve or survive their problems.

People with poor mental health, on the other hand, are more likely to have conflicting feelings about major aspects of life and exhibit relatively poor forethought and self-discipline. They may participate in destructive interpersonal behavior (such as antagonizing people) even though they may be unaware of it. They also have many intense, self-centered desires. Poor mental health is not the same as mental illness.

SELF-ACTUALIZATION

People who are self-actualized have come to terms with life, personal potential and their own place in the world. They seem to be involved in a cause external to themselves. They have an obvious drive that can seem like a calling to ultimate values such as truth, beauty and perfection. If they are truly self-actualized, they are comfortable with themselves and their lives. It has been said that a self-actualized person has reached the highest level of mental health.

Self-actualization means taking responsibility for looking at oneself and being honest. It demands self-awareness and involves moving in the direction of realizing one's full potential.

(continued...)

SELF-ESTEEM AND MENTAL HEALTH

CHARACTERISTICS OF MENTALLY HEALTHY PEOPLE

Mentally healthy people have the following characteristics:

1. They are able and willing to assume responsibilities appropriate to their age.
2. They participate with pleasure in experiences belonging to each successive stage in the life cycle, neither holding on to those of an earlier period nor anticipating those of a later period.
3. They willingly accept the experiences and responsibilities of their role or position in life, even though they may object to the role or position.
4. They attack problems that require solutions, rather than finding ways to evade them.
5. They enjoy attacking and eliminating obstacles to personal development and happiness, after they are convinced that the obstacles are real, not imaginary.
6. They make decisions with a minimum of worry, conflict, advice seeking, or other forms of running-away behavior.
7. They abide by a choice they have made until new factors of crucial importance enter the picture.
8. They find major satisfaction in actual accomplishments and experiences of life rather than in wishful thinking.
9. They know that thinking is a blueprint for action, not a device for delaying or escaping action.
10. They learn from defeats instead of finding excuses for them.
11. They neither magnify successes nor extend their applications from the areas in which they originally occurred.
12. They know how to work when working and how to play when playing.
13. They say no to situations that, over time, run counter to their best interests, even though these situations may provide temporary satisfaction.
14. They say yes to situations that will ultimately aid them, even though these situations may be momentarily unpleasant.
15. They can show anger directly when injured and defend their rights with indignation and action appropriate in kind and amount to the injury.
16. They show affection directly and give evidence of it in actions that are fitting in amount and kind.
17. They can endure pain and emotional frustration whenever it is not in their power to alter the cause.

(continued...)

SELF-ESTEEM AND MENTAL HEALTH

18. They have their habits and mental attitudes well organized so that they can quickly make necessary compromises called for by difficulties they meet.
19. They can concentrate their energies on a single goal they are determined to achieve.
20. They do not try to change the fact that life is an endless struggle; instead, they know that people who fight themselves least will have the most strength and best judgment for the outside battle.
21. They can develop and maintain family and other intimate relationships.

Source: Characteristics of Mentally Healthy People were adapted from C. E. Bruess and G. Richardson. 1995. *Decisions for Health*. Dubuque, IA: W. C. Brown.

PROMOTING POSITIVE SELF-ESTEEM

TIME

1–2 periods

ACTIVITIES

1. Assessing Self-Esteem

2. Promoting Self-Esteem

3. Positive Attributes

4. Improving Crabwell's Self-Esteem

PROMOTING POSITIVE SELF-ESTEEM

OBJECTIVE

Students will be able to:

> Describe personal actions that can improve self-esteem.

GETTING STARTED

Have:

- paper and art supplies
- classroom set of **The Murder of Crabwell Grommet (1.1)**, from Unit 1

Copy for each student:

- Self-Esteem Assessment (3.1)
- Self-Esteem Log (3.2)

UNIT OVERVIEW

PURPOSE

This unit deals with attitudes about self. It emphasizes the personal assessment of self-esteem and encourages students to look realistically at what they can do to promote self-esteem.

MAIN POINTS

✳   Honestly rating oneself on a variety of characteristics can give a general indication of a level of self-esteem.

✳   Making the most of what we have means being honest with ourselves, being flexible, setting attainable goals and seeking help when needed.

✳   Self-esteem can be enhanced by using positive verbalization, accepting what is liked and appreciated about you by others, and including daily activities that will provide a strong likelihood for success.

REVIEW

To increase your understanding of ways to improve self-esteem, review **Promoting Self-Esteem** *Instant Expert* (p. 37).

VOCABULARY

dynamic—Constantly changing.

emotional response—The feeling a person experiences as a reaction to a situation or event.

goal—An end that a person aims to reach or accomplish.

introspection—Looking into one's own mind, feelings, etc.

negative self-talk—Communication with oneself that diminishes or denies one's good qualities.

success—A favorable or satisfactory outcome or result.

1. Assessing Self-Esteem

◖ A Self-Assessment Activity ◗

Students assess self-esteem

Distribute the Self-Esteem Assessment activity sheet and have students complete it. Emphasize that students do not have to share their results, so they can be completely honest.

Students score assessments

Explain the scoring system and have students figure their scores.

Discuss assessment

Discuss student reactions to the assessment. Ask students what they can do if they have a score that indicates negative self-esteem.

Ongoing Assessment Students should begin to realize that self-esteem is dynamic and ever-changing. Look for understanding that changes in self-esteem are normal and can be expected and that people can take action to improve self-esteem.

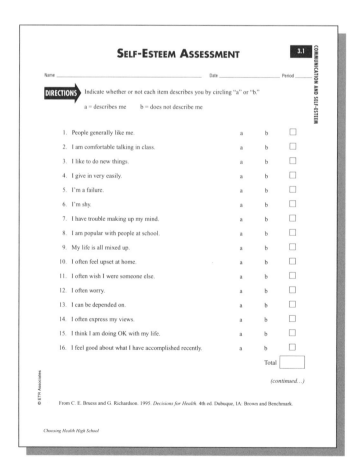

SELF-ESTEEM ASSESSMENT

3.1

Name _____   Date _____   Period _____

DIRECTIONS ▸ Indicate whether or not each item describes you by circling "a" or "b."

a = describes me   b = does not describe me

1. People generally like me.   a   b   ☐
2. I am comfortable talking in class.   a   b   ☐
3. I like to do new things.   a   b   ☐
4. I give in very easily.   a   b   ☐
5. I'm a failure.   a   b   ☐
6. I'm shy.   a   b   ☐
7. I have trouble making up my mind.   a   b   ☐
8. I am popular with people at school.   a   b   ☐
9. My life is all mixed up.   a   b   ☐
10. I often feel upset at home.   a   b   ☐
11. I often wish I were someone else.   a   b   ☐
12. I often worry.   a   b   ☐
13. I can be depended on.   a   b   ☐
14. I often express my views.   a   b   ☐
15. I think I am doing OK with my life.   a   b   ☐
16. I feel good about what I have accomplished recently. a   b   ☐

Total ☐

(continued...)

From C. E. Bruess and G. Richardson. 1995. *Decisions for Health.* 4th ed. Dubuque, IA: Brown and Benchmark.

Choosing Health High School

2. PROMOTING SELF-ESTEEM

Discuss self-esteem

Discuss ways to promote self-esteem, using the **Promoting Self-Esteem** *Instant Expert* as a guide.

Discuss communication that promotes esteem

Ask students if they have ever "felt bad" after someone made a negative comment to them. Challenge students to consider why they may have experienced a "bad" feeling simply from words. Explain that these feelings are connected to self-esteem.

Students demonstrate positive communication

Ask for 2 volunteers to demonstrate the exchange of positive comments. Students can mention a positive personality characteristic or a physical feature. Examples:

- I really like the color of your hair.
- I admire the way you are always able to make the best of a bad situation.

Students exchange positive comments

Have students walk around the classroom and spend about 30 seconds with each person in the class. The assignment is to tell each person something positive.

Recap activity

Ask for volunteers to describe how they felt giving compliments and how they felt receiving them.

20 minutes

✳

SHARPEN THE SKILL
COMMUNICATION—
POSITIVE COMMENTS

Challenge students to express only positive comments to friends and family for a week. Discuss the activity after the week. Were they successful? Was it difficult? Did others communicate more positively?

3. POSITIVE ATTRIBUTES

20 minutes

MATERIALS

◆ paper and art supplies

MEETING STUDENT NEEDS

Be aware of students who may be having trouble thinking of attributes and be ready to offer some suggestions. Emphasize that drawing ability is not the criteria for success in this activity.

✳

Students express attributes

Have students list their own positive attributes. Then ask them to choose one to express in an artistic way. Encourage them to choose an expression that demonstrates a strength in one of their multiple intelligences. Examples:

- a drawing or collage
- a poem
- a play
- a song
- a written description
- a riddle or problem to be solved
- a model or something constructed

Display student work

With students' permission, display the projects in the classroom.

4. IMPROVING CRABWELL'S SELF-ESTEEM

Review story

Distribute **The Murder of Crabwell Grommet** student reading page and ask students to review it, looking for things Crabwell Grommet could have done to improve his self-esteem.

List ways to improve self-esteem

Explain that having a healthy lifestyle can help people feel good about themselves. With this in mind, ask students to suggest ways Crabwell could have improved his self-esteem. Examples:

- stop smoking
- make sound nutritional choices
- deal with his stress in positive ways
- avoid use of alcohol or use it only in moderation
- avoid use of sleeping pills
- get regular exercise
- have friends or family to talk to who can help work out problems

Ask students for any other ways people can improve self-esteem. Make a master list (on the board or butcher paper) of things students suggest as ways for Crabwell and others to improve self-esteem. Post the list and ask students to add suggestions as the course progresses based on their own experiences.

Ongoing Assessment Periodically discuss self-esteem with students and ask for examples of how they or others have improved self-esteem. Ask them to evaluate the effectiveness of the different techniques. Assess students' ability to identify specific, positive strategies.

15 minutes

MATERIALS

- classroom set of The Murder of Crabwell Grommet (1.1), from Unit 1

EVALUATION

10 minutes, plus time for log entries

REVIEW

♦ Promoting Self-Esteem *Instant Expert* (p. 37)

MATERIALS

♦ Self-Esteem Log (3.2)

OBJECTIVE

Students will be able to:

> **Describe personal actions that can improve self-esteem.**

Distribute the **Self-Esteem Log** evaluation sheet. Explain that students are to list things they can do to help themselves or others build positive self-esteem and keep a log of their experiences for 3 days. They should be able to describe how each thing helps build positive self-esteem and how effective the activities they list were at building positive self-esteem. They should describe outcomes of their behaviors.

CRITERIA

Review students' logs for strategies to promote and enhance self-esteem. Examples include being honest with oneself, being flexible, setting attainable goals, seeking help and accepting compliments. See the **Promoting Self-Esteem Instant Expert** for other evaluation criteria.

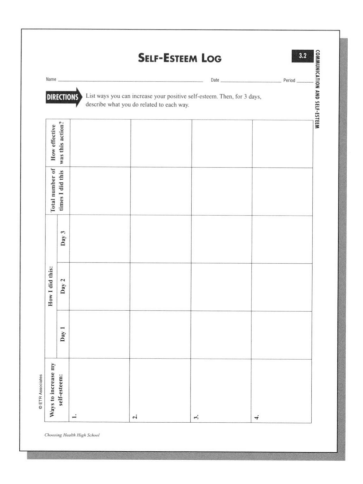

PROMOTING SELF-ESTEEM

Health behavior is influenced by attitudes. Our attitudes about ourselves (self-esteem) are a very important influence on our behavior.

How can we help students assess their level of self-esteem? While many sophisticated instruments might be used, a simple way involves honestly rating oneself on a variety of characteristics that give a general indication of a level of self-esteem. The following questions can provide valuable information about one's level of self-esteem.

- **Do people generally like me?** While there are exceptions to any rule, if people like us, we tend to feel better about ourselves. It also should be pointed out that if we feel positively about ourselves, so will others—it works both ways.

- **Am I comfortable talking in front of others?** If so, I probably have confidence about my knowledge and my communication skills.

- **Do I like to do new things?** If I don't, perhaps it is because I am afraid I'll fail or look silly, or that I won't know how to do them.

- **Do I give in easily?** While it can sometimes be very positive to compromise or even give in to another person's wishes, to do so consistently might be a sign of a lack of good feelings about one's own viewpoint or desire.

- **Do I feel I'm a failure?** Obviously, if so, one can hardly have high self-esteem. However, it might be wise to consider what failure means to each person—failure at what? Is it necessary to succeed at everything? What proportion of failures and successes is one willing to accept?

- **Am I shy?** Since communication skills are related to self-esteem, the answer to this question can be revealing.

- **Do I have trouble making up my mind?** The answer to this question, too, can reflect confidence or a lack of it. While decision making is complex and is related to many considerations, a lack of confidence in the ability to make up one's mind can be evidence of low self-esteem.

- **Do I often feel upset?** We all might feel upset or confused from time to time, but a consistent pattern of these feelings indicates something about self-esteem. Worry is natural, but frequent worrying can be a result of low self-esteem.

- **Do I want to be like someone else?** Often wishing to be like someone else can be an indicator of low self-esteem. It can be fine to try to emulate

(continued...)

PROMOTING SELF-ESTEEM

some characteristics of a positive role model, but to consistently want to be like someone else can mean one is not happy with oneself.

- **Can others depend on me?** Whether or not I feel I can be depended on shows how confident I am about my ability and desire to come through when someone else needs me.
- **Do I express my views?** If I don't think well of myself, I am unlikely to do so very often. If I have positive self-esteem, I will be willing to "expose" myself and my thoughts to others.
- **Do I think I'm doing OK in my life? Do I feel good about what I have accomplished recently?** These 2 questions provide an important summary of self-esteem. They force an evaluation on a broad scale of how one feels about the overall picture.

Prolonged low self-esteem can be a problem if not identified and nurtured. Honestly assessing a personal level of self-esteem and striving to improve it when needed can go a long way toward improving mental health and preventing potential difficulties.

WAYS TO PROMOTE SELF-ESTEEM

Each person is unique and special. Making the most of what we each have is important. Several guidelines can help people do this. These include:

- Be honest with yourself.
- Be flexible.
- Set attainable goals.
- Seek help when it is needed.

Be honest with yourself. Being honest with oneself is essential. We cannot determine whether we are really happy unless we are honest. Honestly acknowledging personal strengths and weaknesses is an important part of this step. Only when we honestly admit that weaknesses exist can anything be done about them. Realizing strengths is also important to personal understanding, as is giving credit where credit is due.

Be flexible. Flexibility is the ability to adjust to changing situations without too much difficulty. A person who can do this usually finds such situations far less stressful. Things do not always go the way we had hoped or planned. We can assess flexibility by looking at some true or imagined situations that require flexibility and honestly assessing how we would react. This assessment can help us develop more and better ways to be flexible.

(continued...)

Promoting Self-Esteem

Set attainable goals. Each of us has different abilities. Our goals, therefore, cannot all be the same. Honestly looking at personal abilities and personal desires can help a person develop both short-term and long-term goals. Although some goals should be a little beyond our reach, most goals should be attainable, or we set ourselves up for constant failure. Determining personal goals helps us decide which activities or projects fit these goals and which don't. Such knowledge is a valuable aid in decision making.

Seek help when it is needed. We generally need others to communicate with, express emotions to and get feedback from. Seeking help from others can be very healthy—it can help us avoid problems in the first place and assist us in dealing with any problems that develop.

ENHANCING SELF-ESTEEM

Specific actions can help enhance self-esteem. These include:
- using positive verbalization
- accepting compliments
- planning for success

Use positive verbalization. Positive verbalization involves writing down positive personality traits that one likes about oneself and reflecting on those traits. It includes continuing to identify positive traits. Reflective time spent dwelling on positive traits helps enhance self-esteem. Positive verbalization can counter negative self-talk.

Accept compliments. Leaning to accept compliments from others helps enhance self-esteem. We can learn to accept compliments by saying "thank you" rather than shrugging them off or denying that our positive characteristics exist.

Plan for success. Planning to be regularly involved in activities one does well helps enhance self-esteem. We can choose activities in which we have a strong likelihood of success. For example: Play a game at which you do well. Do the homework in your better subjects first. Make it a point to talk with someone who loves you. Most important, enjoy the experience!

STEP BY STEP

TIME

1 period

ACTIVITIES

1. What's the Problem

2. The Decision-Making Process

3. The Decision Tree

4. Decision-Making Dilemmas

STEP BY STEP

OBJECTIVES

Students will be able to:

> 1. Describe specific steps that can be used for problem solving and decision making.

> 2. Demonstrate steps in problem solving and decision making.

GETTING STARTED

Make transparency of:

- Problem-Solving Steps (4.1)
- Decision Tree Example (4.3)
- Decision Tree (4.4) (*Optional:* Make several transparencies for use in Activity 4.)

Copy a classroom set of:

- Problem Solving Skills (4.2)

Copy 1 for each group:

- Decision Tree (4.4)

Copy for each student:

- Decision Tree (4.4)
- Decision-Making Dilemmas (4.5)

UNIT OVERVIEW

PURPOSE

Skills influence health behavior because they allow people to apply attitudes and knowledge to everyday situations. This unit helps improve students' skills for problem solving and decision making.

MAIN POINTS

* Many decisions are made without consideration of all aspects of the problem.
* Problem-solving steps include perceiving the problem, owning the problem, breaking the problem into smaller parts, gathering information, formulating trial solutions, and taking action.
* Many factors influence decision making and problem solving.
* Decision making, even when properly done, leads to the need to make additional decisions.

REVIEW

To increase your understanding of problem-solving and decision-making processes, review **Problem Solving and Decision Making** *Instant Expert* (p. 51).

VOCABULARY	
brainstorming—Listing all possible ideas, without judging or eliminating any.	**decision**—The act of making up one's mind; a judgment or conclusion.

1. WHAT'S THE PROBLEM?

10 minutes

SHARPEN THE SKILL

**GOAL SETTING—
PLANNING FOR SUCCESS**

A key factor in solving problems involves planning. Have students identify a goal that is related to one of the problems discussed. As a class, identify possible steps in a plan to reach the goal. Have students identify appropriate rewards for reaching the goal.

Students brainstorm problems

Ask students what problems teens most frequently face. List responses on the board.

Discuss solving problems

Discuss how teens usually solve problems, using questions such as the following to frame the discussion:

- How much time do teens spend on solving problems?
- What methods do teens often use to solve problems?
- How do teens consider their choices?
- What influences choices?
- Do teens' choices usually work?
- What might teens do to make their choices work better?

Ongoing Assessment Look for students to draw conclusions about things that may need work related to solving problems. For example:

- Teens need to spend conscious time thinking through solutions.
- Some teens just react.
- Some teens don't consider a variety of solutions.

2. THE DECISION-MAKING PROCESS

Discuss decision making

Present a mini-lecture on decision making, using the **Problem-Solving Steps** transparency. Emphasize the 6-step process. As each step is described, ask students to discuss what factors will influence that step of the decision-making process.

Dyads apply steps

Identify a problem related to health. Have students work in dyads to apply the 6-step process from the transparency. Ask them to write down their ideas for each of the 6 steps. Distribute the **Problem Solving Skills** student reading page for use during the dyad discussion.

Discuss dyad work

Review the various comments and suggestions developed by dyad discussion. Summarize the points presented on the board.

   Collect the student reading pages for reuse.

20 minutes

MATERIALS

♦ transparency of Problem Solving Steps (4.1)
♦ classroom set of Problem Solving Skills (4.2)

PROBLEM-SOLVING STEPS `4.1`

1. Recognize the problem.

2. Own the problem.

3. Break the problem into smaller parts.

4. Gather information.

5. Formulate trial solutions.

6. Act now.

© ETR Associates

Choosing Health High School

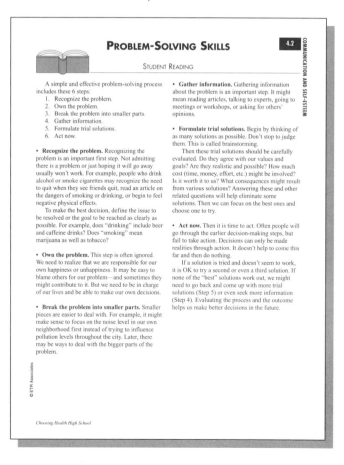

PROBLEM-SOLVING SKILLS `4.2`

STUDENT READING

A simple and effective problem-solving process includes these 6 steps:
1. Recognize the problem.
2. Own the problem.
3. Break the problem into smaller parts.
4. Gather information.
5. Formulate trial solutions.
6. Act now.

• **Recognize the problem.** Recognizing the problem is an important first step. Not admitting there is a problem or just hoping it will go away usually won't work. For example, people who drink alcohol or smoke cigarettes may recognize the need to quit when they see friends quit, read an article on the dangers of smoking or drinking, or begin to feel negative physical effects.
   To make the best decision, define the issue to be resolved or the goal to be reached as clearly as possible. For example, does "drinking" include beer and caffeine drinks? Does "smoking" mean marijuana as well as tobacco?

• **Own the problem.** This step is often ignored. We need to realize that we are responsible for our own happiness or unhappiness. It may be easy to blame others for our problem—and sometimes they might contribute to it. But we need to be in charge of our lives and be able to make our own decisions.

• **Break the problem into smaller parts.** Smaller pieces are easier to deal with. For example, it might make sense to focus on the noise level in our own neighborhood first instead of trying to influence pollution levels throughout the city. Later, there may be ways to deal with the bigger parts of the problem.

• **Gather information.** Gathering information about the problem is an important step. It might mean reading articles, talking to experts, going to meetings or workshops, or asking for others' opinions.

• **Formulate trial solutions.** Begin by thinking of as many solutions as possible. Don't stop to judge them. This is called brainstorming.
   Then these trial solutions should be carefully evaluated. Do they agree with our values and goals? Are they realistic and possible? How much cost (time, money, effort, etc.) might be involved? Is it worth it to us? What consequences might result from various solutions? Answering these and other related questions will help eliminate some solutions. Then we can focus on the best ones and choose one to try.

• **Act now.** Then it is time to act. Often people will go through the earlier decision-making steps, but fail to take action. Decisions can only be made realities through action. It doesn't help to come this far and then do nothing.
   If a solution is tried and doesn't seem to work, it is OK to try a second or even a third solution. If none of the "best" solutions work out, we might need to go back and come up with more trial solutions (Step 5) or even seek more information (Step 4). Evaluating the process and the outcome helps us make better decisions in the future.

© ETR Associates

Choosing Health High School

3. THE DECISION TREE

10 minutes

*

MATERIALS

- transparency of Decision Tree Example (4.3)
- transparency of Decision Tree (4.4)
- Decision Tree (4.4)
- classroom set of The Murder of Crabwell Grommet (1.1), from Unit 1

*

Discuss decision tree

Display the **Decision Tree Example** transparency, which diagrams a decision about not drinking alcohol at a party. Use it to review the choices and possible actions to take in the decision-making process.

Ask students to identify a common health decision faced by teens. Work through the possible choices, using a blank transparency of the **Decision Tree** activity sheet to illustrate how each decision can lead to other decisions.

Groups prepare decision tree

Divide the class into small groups of 3–4. Give each group a copy of the **Decision Tree** activity sheet and **The Murder of Crabwell Grommet** student reading page. Explain the group assignment:

- Review the story of Crabwell Grommet and discuss some of the decisions he made.
- Choose 1 of these decisions and work through all the choices Crabwell could have made.

(continued...)

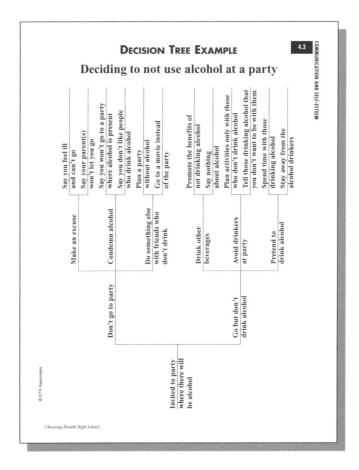

DECISION TREE EXAMPLE 4.3

Deciding to not use alcohol at a party

Invited to party where there will be alcohol

Don't go to party
- Make an excuse
  - Say you feel ill and can't go
  - Say your parent(s) won't let you go
- Condemn alcohol
  - Say you won't go to a party where alcohol is present
  - Say you don't like people who drink alcohol
- Do something else with friends who don't drink
  - Plan a party without alcohol
  - Go to a movie instead of the party

Go but don't drink alcohol
- Drink other beverages
  - Promote the benefits of not drinking alcohol
  - Say nothing about alcohol
- Avoid drinkers at party
  - Plan activities only with those who don't drink alcohol
  - Tell those drinking alcohol that you don't want to be with them
- Pretend to drink alcohol
  - Spend time with those drinking alcohol
  - Stay away from the alcohol drinkers

COMMUNICATION AND SELF-ESTEEM

© ETR Associates

Choosing Health High School

3. THE DECISION TREE

(CONTINUED)

- Fill in the choices on the **Decision Tree** activity sheet and be prepared to share your work with the class.
- For the last branches in the tree, identify the consequences of each behavior. Groups should use the discussion of consequences as a basis for the choice.

Groups report

Have groups report their choices. Discuss each group's decision and the choices they made.

Ongoing Assessment Look for students to begin to make conclusions about cause and effect regarding health choices. They should also demonstrate an understanding of the complexity of issues and choices that relate to health, and be able to identify consequences associated with each choice.

SHARPEN THE SKILL

DECISION MAKING—THINKING OF CONSEQUENCES

Write the word *consequences* on the board. Discuss the meaning of the word as a class. Then put students into dyads. Have them select a situation in which a decision must be made and brainstorm examples of both positive and negative consequences.

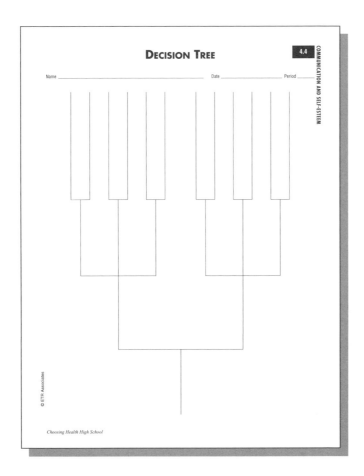

DECISION TREE

Name _____ Date _____ Period _____

COMMUNICATION AND SELF-ESTEEM

© ETR Associates

Choosing Health High School

4. DECISION-MAKING DILEMMAS

15 minutes

✳

MATERIALS
- Decision Tree (4.4)
- Decision-Making Dilemmas (4.5)
- *Optional:* transparencies of Decision Tree (4.4)

✳

Groups solve dilemmas

Divide the class into small groups of 3–4. Distribute the **Decision Tree** and **Decision-Making Dilemmas** activity sheets. Have students use the 6-step problem-solving process to examine 1 of the dilemmas and solve it using the decision tree. Be sure each dilemma is covered by at least 1 group.

Note: Groups should use the 6-step process as a basis for discussion about the problem. In a classroom setting, it is not possible to actually apply all steps.

Discuss solutions

Ask groups to share how they solved a particular dilemma. You might want to fill out a blank transparency of the **Decision Tree** activity sheet for each dilemma during the discussion. Discuss possible consequences for each behavior on the **Decision Tree**. Looking at consequences is part of evaluating the trial solutions. "Act now" is the final step, or the solution.

(continued...)

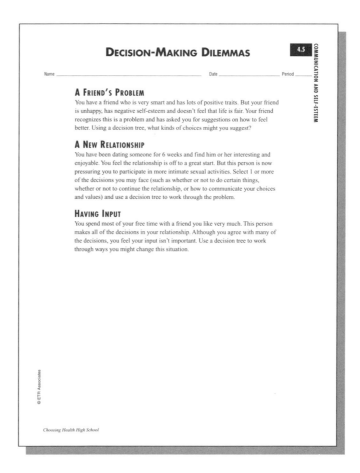

DECISION-MAKING DILEMMAS   4.5

Name _____ Date _____ Period _____

A FRIEND'S PROBLEM
You have a friend who is very smart and has lots of positive traits. But your friend is unhappy, has negative self-esteem and doesn't feel that life is fair. Your friend recognizes this is a problem and has asked you for suggestions on how to feel better. Using a decision tree, what kinds of choices might you suggest?

A NEW RELATIONSHIP
You have been dating someone for 6 weeks and find him or her interesting and enjoyable. You feel the relationship is off to a great start. But this person is now pressuring you to participate in more intimate sexual activities. Select 1 or more of the decisions you may face (such as whether or not to do certain things, whether or not to continue the relationship, or how to communicate your choices and values) and use a decision tree to work through the problem.

HAVING INPUT
You spend most of your free time with a friend you like very much. This person makes all of the decisions in your relationship. Although you agree with many of the decisions, you feel your input isn't important. Use a decision tree to work through ways you might change this situation.

© ETR Associates

Choosing Health High School

4. DECISION-MAKING DILEMMAS

CONTINUED

Students write dilemmas to solve (optional)

Divide the class into pairs and have each student write about a probable dilemma for teens. Ask students to trade papers with their partners, who will write a possible solution to the dilemma. Have 3–5 volunteers share the results with the class.

Ongoing Assessment Look for students' ability to apply the problem-solving steps to make decisions and solve problems in a health-enhancing manner.

SHARPEN THE SKILL

DECISION MAKING— STORIES ABOUT CONSEQUENCES

The ability to identify possible consequences to any decision is very important. Have students write and illustrate children's stories that teach about consequences. They could read their stories to students in local elementary schools.

EVALUATION

OBJECTIVE 1

Students will be able to:

> **Describe specific steps that can be used for problem solving and decision making.**

Observe students as they describe the steps during dyad discussion in Activity 2.

CRITERIA

See the **Problem Solving and Decision Making** *Instant Expert* for evaluation criteria. Steps should include:

1. Recognize the problem.
2. Own the problem.
3. Break the problem into smaller parts.
4. Gather information.
5. Formulate trial solutions.
6. Act now.

OBJECTIVE 2

Students will be able to:

> **Demonstrate steps in problem solving and decision making.**

Review students' work on the **Decision Tree** activity sheet and ask them to describe steps in problem solving and decision making. Students may choose to act out their solutions.

CRITERIA

Students should be assessed on their ability to recognize and show several of the problem-solving steps. *Note:* It may not be possible to demonstrate every step, nor will every step be necessary to every situation. Look for students to demonstrate a logical process that includes many of the problem-solving steps.

5 minutes

MATERIALS

◆ completed Decision Tree (4.4), from Activity 4

PROBLEM SOLVING AND DECISION MAKING

Problem solving and decision making are continual processes. One decision often leads to the need to make more decisions. This is natural and should not be cause for worry.

The skills of problem solving and decision making can be described in various ways. One simple and effective method for learning and practicing these skills includes the following 6 steps:

1. Recognize the problem.
2. Own the problem.
3. Break the problem into smaller parts.
4. Gather information.
5. Formulate trial solutions.
6. Act now.

THE DECISION-MAKING STEPS

Recognize the problem. Recognizing the problem is an important first step. Not acknowledging a continuing discomfort or believing it will go away is not likely to result in a satisfactory solution.

People who drink alcohol or smoke cigarettes, for example, may recognize the need to quit when they see friends quit, read an article on the dangers of smoking or drinking, or begin to feel negative physical effects.

To make the best decision, we should define the issue to be resolved or the goal to be reached as clearly as possible. For example, does "drinking" include beer and caffeine drinks? Does "smoking" mean marijuana as well as tobacco?

Own the problem. This step is often ignored. We need to realize that we are responsible for our happiness or unhappiness. It may be easy to blame others for our problem (and sometimes they might contribute to it), but we need to be in charge of our lives and be able to make our own decisions.

Break the problem into smaller parts. This step gives us a more manageable piece with which to deal. For example, if we feel our environment is a problem, it might make sense to focus on the noise level in our neighborhood first instead of trying to influence pollution levels throughout the city. Later, there may be ways to deal with the bigger parts of the problem.

Gather information. Gathering information about the problem is an important fact-finding step. It might mean reading articles on specific topics, talking to experts, attending meetings or workshops, or asking for others' opinions.

(continued...)

PROBLEM SOLVING AND DECISION MAKING

Formulate trial solutions. Begin by thinking of as many solutions as possible without stopping to evaluate them. This process is called brainstorming.

Then the trial solutions should be carefully evaluated. Do they agree with our values and goals? Are they realistic and possible? How much cost (time, money, effort, etc.) might be involved? Is it worth it to us? What consequences might result from various solutions? Answering these and other related questions will help eliminate some of the solutions and allow us to focus on the best ones, from which we will need to select one to try.

Act now. Finally, it is time to act. Often people will go through the earlier decision-making steps, but fail to take action. Decisions can only be implemented through action. It does little good to come this far and then do nothing.

If a solution is tried and doesn't work, it is OK to try a second or even a third solution. If none of the "best" solutions work out, it might be necessary to go back and consider additional trial solutions (Step 5) or even seek more information (Step 4) about the problem. Evaluating the process and the outcome helps us make better decisions in the future.

UNIT
5

TYPES OF COMMUNICATION

TIME

1–2 periods

ACTIVITIES

1. Psst, Pass It On!

2. Types of Communication

3. What Do You See?

4. Nonverbal Communication

5. Communicating with Crabwell Grommet

TYPES OF COMMUNICATION

Students will be able to:

1. Explain the different levels of communication.

2. Demonstrate nonverbal communication.

3. Describe ways to promote self-esteem by improving communication skills.

GETTING STARTED

Have:

- blank paper
- classroom set of **The Murder of Crabwell Grommet (1.1),** from Unit 1

Copy a classroom set of:

- Types of Communication (5.1)

Copy:

- What Do You See 1–3 (5.2)–(5.4)

UNIT OVERVIEW

PURPOSE

This lesson deals with communication and how it contributes to self-esteem. Students have an opportunity to learn more about the types of communication (verbal and nonverbal) and the role of these in communicating. After hearing about the different levels of communication, students roleplay examples of each.

MAIN POINTS

✳ There are 2 basic types of communication: verbal and nonverbal. Nonverbal communication through body language often says as much as the spoken word.

✳ Specific skills are involved in being a good speaker and a good listener.

✳ Most conversations focus on 4 levels of communication.

- Level 1 communication (information giving) is friendly and conventional.
- Level 2 communication (directive or argumentative) involves directing and demanding.
- Level 3 communication (exploratory) is tentative and exploring.
- Level 4 communication (self-disclosing) is disclosing and understanding.

REVIEW

To increase your understanding of communication skills, review *Types of Communication Instant Expert* (p. 64).

VOCABULARY

body language—A form of nonverbal communication made up of facial expressions, body movement, posture, gestures, etc., that are clues to a person's thoughts and feelings.

communication—The ability to express thoughts, feelings and reactions and to exchange information among people.

disclosure—Revealing one's true thoughts and feelings to another.

nonverbal communication—The use of symbols, signs or body language to convey a message.

1-way verbal communication—Information is passed by one person to another with no opportunity for the receiver to provide feedback of any kind.

2-way verbal communication—The process of passing information between speaker and listener with limited feedback.

1. PSST, PASS IT ON!

10 minutes

✳

SHARPEN THE SKILL
COMMUNICATION— TECHNOLOGY AND THE FUTURE

Communication skills are currently evolving with new technology. Assign students a research assignment to investigate new ways people communicate today or will be communicating in the future. Examples include e-mail, computer chat or tele-conferencing.

Discuss communication

Ask students:

- Why is clear communication important?
- Why do we need clear communication?
- What are some of the ways information can be distorted?

Students play game

Explain the Psst, Pass It On! game. It is based on *Telephone*, a classic communication game. Begin the game.

When everyone has heard the message, ask the last student to state what he or she heard. Compare this version to the message you gave the first student.

Recap game

Discuss how this activity relates to real-life situations. Ask students to share some things that might involve communication issues in real life.

Ongoing Assessment Look for students to conclude that clear communication is difficult even in controlled circumstances.

DIRECTIONS FOR GAME

- You (the teacher) will begin by whispering a short (1–2 sentence) message related to this unit to a student.
- That student will then whisper the message to the student behind him or her.
- Continue until everyone in the class has heard the message.
- Students will not be allowed to ask questions or have the message repeated during the game.

2. TYPES OF COMMUNICATION

A DEMONSTRATION ACTIVITY

Discuss verbal and nonverbal communication

Define verbal and nonverbal communication and discuss the levels of verbal communication, using the **Types of Communication** *Instant Expert* as a guide. Ask students to consider factors that are important in each kind of communication. For example, verbal communication involves words, but tone and inflection can influence the interpretation of those words. Nonverbal aspects, such as contact or body posture also send a message.

Distribute the **Types of Communication** student reading page and have students review it.

Brainstorm examples

Ask students to brainstorm examples of verbal and nonverbal communication. Challenge them to think about the impact of the specific communication on relationships.

If students are willing, ask them to demonstrate or cite examples of use of the different levels of conversation. Have the class vote on the examples that were most effective.

Collect the student reading pages for reuse.

10 minutes

MATERIALS

♦ classroom set of Types of Communication (5.1)

FAMILY LINK

Suggest to students that they play the Psst, Pass It On! game with their families. It is something that could be done as a part of a celebration gathering. Ask students to interview families about clear communication in the family.

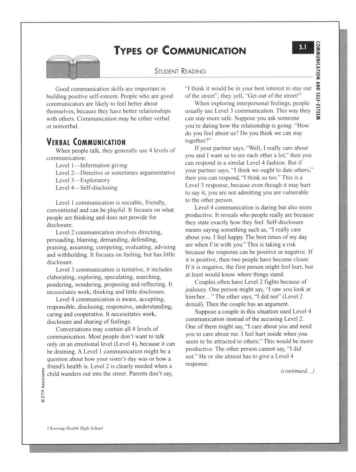

TYPES OF COMMUNICATION
5.1

STUDENT READING

Good communication skills are important in building positive self-esteem. People who are good communicators are likely to feel better about themselves, because they have better relationships with others. Communication may be either verbal or nonverbal.

VERBAL COMMUNICATION
When people talk, they generally use 4 levels of communication:
Level 1—Information giving
Level 2—Directive or sometimes argumentative
Level 3—Exploratory
Level 4—Self-disclosing

Level 1 communication is sociable, friendly, conventional and can be playful. It focuses on what people are thinking and does not provide for disclosure.
Level 2 communication involves directing, persuading, blaming, demanding, defending, praising, assuming, competing, evaluating, advising and withholding. It focuses on feeling, but has little disclosure.
Level 3 communication is tentative, it includes elaborating, exploring, speculating, searching, pondering, wondering, proposing and reflecting. It necessitates work, thinking and little disclosure.
Level 4 communication is aware, accepting, responsible, disclosing, responsive, understanding, caring and cooperative. It necessitates work, disclosure and sharing of feelings.
Conversations may contain all 4 levels of communication. Most people don't want to talk only on an emotional level (Level 4), because it can be draining. A Level 1 communication might be a question about how your sister's day was or how a friend's health is. Level 2 is clearly needed when a child wanders out into the street. Parents don't say,

"I think it would be in your best interest to stay out of the street"; they yell, "Get out of the street!"
When exploring interpersonal feelings, people usually use Level 3 communication. This way they can stay more safe. Suppose you ask someone you're dating how the relationship is going: "How do you feel about us? Do you think we can stay together?"
If your partner says, "Well, I really care about you and I want us to see each other a lot," then you can respond in a similar Level 4 fashion. But if your partner says, "I think we ought to date others," then you can respond, "I think so too." This is a Level 3 response, because even though it may hurt to say it, you are not admitting you are vulnerable to the other person.
Level 4 communication is daring but also more productive. It reveals who people really are because they state exactly how they feel. Self-disclosure means saying something such as, "I really care about you. I feel happy. The best times of my day are when I'm with you." This is taking a risk because the response can be positive or negative. If it is positive, then two people have become closer. If it is negative, the first person might feel hurt, but at least would know where things stand.
Couples often have Level 2 fights because of jealousy. One person might say, "I saw you look at him/her..." The other says, "I did not" (Level 2 denial). Then the couple has an argument.
Suppose a couple in this situation used Level 4 communication instead of the accusing Level 2. One of them might say, "I care about you and need you to care about me. I feel hurt inside when you seem to be attracted to others." This would be more productive. The other person cannot say, "I did not." He or she almost has to give a Level 4 response.

(continued...)

© ETR Associates

Choosing Health High School

3. WHAT DO YOU SEE?

15 minutes

MATERIALS

◆ blank paper
◆ What Do You See? 1–3 (5.2)–(5.4)

Introduce experiment

Ask for 3 students to volunteer to come to the front of the class. Give each volunteer a different **What Do You See?** drawing. Each drawing has a different design and instructions on it. Tell students that they will be drawing a design described by each volunteer. Indicate that the instructions will change for each design.

Students draw designs according to instructions

Distribute blank paper to the class. One at a time, have the volunteers verbally describe the designs to the class. Students draw the designs according to the volunteers' instructions. Be sure that only volunteer 3 answers questions from the class verbally. Students may draw all 3 designs on the same piece of paper, but should indicate number 1, 2 or 3 on the drawing.

(continued...)

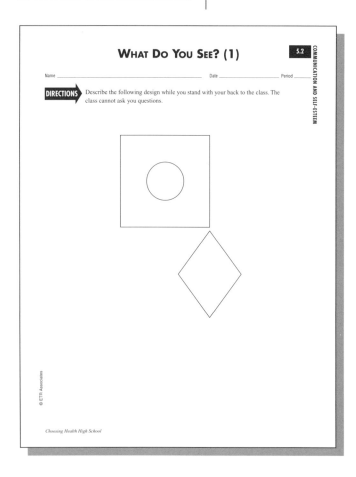

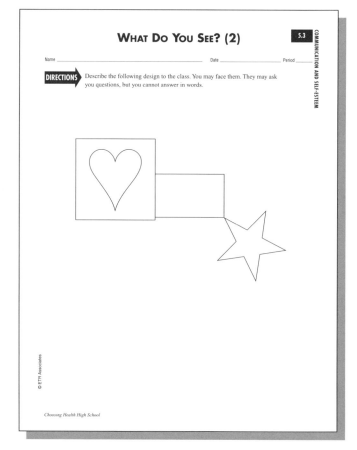

3. What Do You See?

Discuss experiment

Have students reveal their work to each other. Discuss the differences among the instructions students received:

- Drawing 1—total 1-way verbal communication
- Drawing 2—1-way verbal communication with nonverbal feedback
- Drawing 3—2-way verbal communication

Ask students: Which instructions were most effective? Why? With students' permission, display the drawings in the classroom.

Ongoing Assessment Look for students to conclude that there is an increased ability to understand another person when they are permitted to interact with the person.

SHARPEN THE SKILL

COMMUNICATION— YOUR OWN DESIGN

Have students create their own designs and conduct the experiment again. Ask students if they learned from the previous experience and were better able to communicate.

✳

WHAT DO YOU SEE? (3)

 5.4

COMMUNICATION AND SELF-ESTEEM

Name _____ Date _____ Period _____

DIRECTIONS Describe the following design to the class. They may ask you questions and you may answer.

© ETR Associates

Choosing Health High School

4. NONVERBAL COMMUNICATION

A SMALL GROUP ACTIVITY

20 minutes

EXTEND THE LEARNING

Ask students to become observers of body language for 24 hours. Allow class time to discuss their observations.

✳

Groups identify body language

Divide the class into small groups of 5–6. Explain the group assignment:

- List ways you can tell how people are feeling without observing their speech.
- Discuss the accuracy of words versus the accuracy of behavior.
- Prepare to demonstrate to the class some different body positions (hands on hips, arms crossed, etc.) that communicate feelings.

Groups demonstrate body language

Have each group demonstrate a few types of nonverbal communication, or body language. Ask the class to identify what each position might indicate.

5. COMMUNICATING WITH CRABWELL GROMMET

Groups create roleplays

Divide the class into small groups or leave them in their groups from Activity 4. Distribute **The Murder of Crabwell Grommet** student reading page and explain the group assignment:

- Review the story. Look for some examples of the ways in which Crabwell Grommet communicated.
- Plan a roleplay that demonstrates how Crabwell could have communicated more effectively.

Groups present roleplays

Have groups present their roleplays to the class. Discuss the communication skills groups depict. Ask students how Crabwell Grommet's communication skills might have influenced his self-esteem.

Collect the student reading pages for reuse.

25 minutes

MATERIALS

◆ classroom set of The Murder of Crabwell Grommet (1.1), from Unit 1

SHARPEN THE SKILL

COMMUNICATION— CONVERSATION OPENERS

Conduct a discussion about the relationship self-esteem has to communication. Ask students to brainstorm ways to start a conversation. Practice these "openers" in groups. This can boost self-confidence and self-esteem.

EVALUATION

20 minutes

OBJECTIVE 1

Students will be able to:

Explain the different levels of communication.

Have students write a short essay in which they list the 4 levels of communication and explain each level. Ask them to compare the effectiveness across levels.

CRITERIA

Look for students to explain the increasing degree of personal intimacy across the levels. See the **Types of Communication** *Instant Expert* for evaluation criteria.

OBJECTIVE 2

Students will be able to:

Demonstrate nonverbal communication.

Observe students during the small group work in Activity 4 to assess their ability to demonstrate nonverbal communication.

CRITERIA

Assess students' ability to effectively communicate a feeling or tone through body language.

(continued...)

EVALUATION

OBJECTIVE 3

Students will be able to:

> **Describe ways to promote self-esteem by improving communication skills.**

10 minutes

Have students write about how improving their communication skills can promote self-esteem.

CRITERIA

Look for students to make points such as the following:

- Good communication is important in friendship. Having good relationships with those around us improves self-esteem.
- Clear communication reduces misinterpretation and makes us feel better about ourselves, thus improving self-esteem.
- Body language may help communicate what you are verbalizing and contribute to helping you feel good about yourself.

TYPES OF COMMUNICATION

The skill of communicating effectively is an important component in building positive self-esteem. People who are good communicators are likely to feel better about themselves, because they have better relationships with others. Communication may be either verbal or nonverbal.

VERBAL COMMUNICATION

When people talk, they generally function on 1 of 4 levels of communication:
- Level 1—Information giving
- Level 2—Directive, or sometimes argumentative
- Level 3—Exploratory
- Level 4—Self-disclosing

Level 1 communication is sociable, friendly, conventional and can be playful. It emphasizes thinking and does not provide for disclosure.

Level 2 communication involves directing, persuading, blaming, demanding, defending, praising, assuming, competing, evaluating, advising and withholding. It emphasizes feeling, but has little disclosure.

Level 3 communication is tentative and involves elaborating, exploring, speculating, searching, pondering, wondering, proposing and reflecting. It necessitates work, thinking and little disclosure.

Level 4 communication is aware, accepting, responsible, disclosing, responsive, understanding, caring and cooperative. It necessitates work, disclosure and sharing of feelings.

Conversations may contain all 4 levels of communication. For example, people seldom want to converse only on an emotional level (Level 4), because it can be draining. A Level 1 communication might be a question about how your sister's day was or how a friend's health is. Level 2 is clearly needed when a child wanders out into the street. Parents don't say, "I think it would be in your best interest to stay out of the street"; they yell, "Get out of the street!"

When exploring interpersonal feelings, people usually use Level 3 communication. This type gives them a safeguard. They might ask a partner how the relationship is progressing: "How do you feel about us? Do you think we can stay together?"

If the partner says, "Well, I really care about you and I want us to see each other a lot," one can respond in a similar Level 4 fashion. However, if the partner says, "I think

(continued...)

TYPES OF COMMUNICATION

we ought to date others," one can respond, "I think so too"—a Level 3 response. Even though it may hurt to say it, one isn't vulnerable to the other person.

Level 4 communication is daring but also more productive; it reveals who people really are because they state exactly how they feel. Self-disclosure involves statements such as, "I really care about you. I feel happy. The best times of my day are when I'm with you." Statements such as these involve a risk because the other person's response can be positive or negative. If it is positive, a great deal has been accomplished. If it is negative, the first person might naturally feel hurt or rejected, but at least would know how things stand.

Couples often have Level 2 fights because of jealousy. An accusation such as "I saw you look at him/her…," will usually be met with "I did not" (Level 2 denial) and is usually followed by an argument.

If a couple in this situation used Level 4 communication instead of the accusing Level 2, one of them might say, "I care about you and need you to care about me. I feel hurt inside when you seem to be attracted to others." This would be more productive; the response almost has to be a Level 4 response.

NONVERBAL COMMUNICATION

Nonverbal communication may be even more telling than words. Notice the body posture of students. During an interesting lecture or activity, most of them will probably be leaning or looking toward the lecturer or the center of the group, indicating they are interested and involved. During a boring class, they will probably be leaning away from the lecturer or group. This physical behavior is called body language.

Communication by the posture of the body often says as much as the spoken word. When people feel uncomfortable about expressing their thoughts or feelings verbally, body language is sometimes the only form of communication in which they participate.

We all recognize the importance of communicating nonverbally, since we smile when we say hello, scratch our heads when perplexed and hug a friend to show affection. We even have terms to describe our nonverbal behavior, such as "Keep a stiff upper lip," "I'm tongue-tied," and "He caught her eye."

We show appreciation and affection, revulsion and indifference with facial expressions and gestures. We tell people we are interested in them merely by making eye contact, and we display aspects of our personality by the way we dress and even how we stand.

(continued…)

TYPES OF COMMUNICATION

Unfortunately, the nonverbal expression of feelings and thoughts is easy to misinterpret. Consequently, depending on nonverbal communication alone to express yourself is to risk being misunderstood.

COMMUNICATION PROBLEMS

Regardless of the type or level of communication, poor communication is usually associated with a failure to listen, an attempt to win, an inability to show an understanding of another's viewpoint and a rigidity that prevents consideration of alternative solutions. Obvious problems can result from poor communication. Many of the issues that result in conflicts or even violence are rooted in poor communication.

PROMOTING COMMUNICATION

TIME
2 periods

ACTIVITIES
1. Communication Gap

2. Unsuccessful Communication

3. Successful Communication

4. Practicing Effective Communication

5. Measuring Assertiveness

PROMOTING COMMUNICATION

OBJECTIVES

Students will be able to:

> 1. Identify the components of successful communication.

> 2. Demonstrate effective communication.

GETTING STARTED

Make transparency of:

- The Communication Gap (6.1)

Copy for each student:

- Unsuccessful Communication (6.2)
- Successful Communication (6.3)
- Measure Your Assertiveness (6.4)
- What Would You Say? (6.5)

UNIT OVERVIEW

PURPOSE

Effective communication skills can have a positive influence on health behavior and self-esteem. Activities in this unit help students build their communication skills. They also include steps for resolving interpersonal conflict.

MAIN POINTS

✳ An understanding of different language systems can contribute to good communication.

✳ Successful resolution of interpersonal conflict requires high-level communication, including active listening, identifying one's position and exploring alternative solutions.

✳ Not setting aside time for discussion is a common communication barrier.

✳ Assertiveness is basic to communication, but it must be differentiated from aggressiveness and nonassertiveness.

✳ Communication skills can be improved.

REVIEW

To increase your understanding of communication skills, review *Effective Communication Instant Expert* (p. 80).

VOCABULARY

active listening—Restating another's words to show that the meaning has been understood.

aggressive communication—Standing up for your rights at the expense of someone else's rights.

assertive communication—Standing up for your basic rights without violating someone else's.

communication barrier—Anything which hinders clear communication between the sender and the receiver of a message; any type of interference that can confuse the meaning of the message being sent.

language—Human speech and its written symbols; a means of communicating.

language system—The particular style of verbal expression characteristic of a person, group, profession, etc.

nonassertive communication—Giving up your basic rights so others can achieve theirs.

1. COMMUNICATION GAP

20 minutes

MATERIALS

♦ transparency of The Communication Gap (6.1)

Discuss communication problems

Display **The Communication Gap** transparency and read it with students. Pose the questions on the transparency.

Possible answers to questions:

1. Jim and the physician are not communicating effectively because they are using different language systems. Jim is using street language, while the physician is using medical/scientific language.
2. This problem could have been avoided if both people used the same language system.
3. The situation could have been improved if the physician explained things in terms Jim could understand. It would have been helpful if Jim had not used slang terms.

Clarify language systems

Discuss and differentiate among the 4 language systems, using the **Effective Communication** *Instant Expert* as a guide. Give examples of each system and when it might be used. Explain that it is important to be aware of these systems and to try to communicate in the language system of the other person.

(continued...)

THE COMMUNICATION GAP　　6.1

COMMUNICATION AND SELF-ESTEEM

Jim goes to the doctor because he is feeling pain when urinating. He describes the problem to his doctor, using slang terms that he learned from his friends. His doctor discusses the situation with him, but uses medical terms.

Jim doesn't understand most of these terms. Jim is too embarrassed to ask about the terms, so he leaves feeling frustrated.

1. What is the problem in this situation?
2. How could this communication problem have been avoided?
3. How could this situation have been improved?

©ETR Associates

Choosing Health High School

---

1. COMMUNICATION GAP

CONTINUED

Discuss conflict resolution

Explain that successful conflict resolution requires Level 4 communication, which includes active listening, identifying one's position and exploring alternative solutions.

Describe what is meant by active or reflective listening and indicate how it can be helpful. Stress the importance of setting aside adequate time for discussion.

Differentiate among assertiveness, nonassertiveness and aggressive behavior. Give examples of each type of behavior, using the **Effective Communication** *Instant Expert* as a guide.

SHARPEN THE SKILL

COMMUNICATION— ACTIVE LISTENING PRACTICE

Set up situations in class that require student pairs to listen, then restate the point of view they heard. Suggest that students use the following phrases in their practice: "What I heard you say was…" and, "Did I interpret you correctly?"

---

2. UNSUCCESSFUL COMMUNICATION

10 minutes

MATERIALS

◆ Unsuccessful Communication (6.2)

Read about unsuccessful communication

Distribute the Unsuccessful Communication activity sheet and have students read it.

List factors in communication problems

Conduct a brainstorming session to identify the factors that contributed to the communication problems in the scenario. List responses on the board.

(continued...)

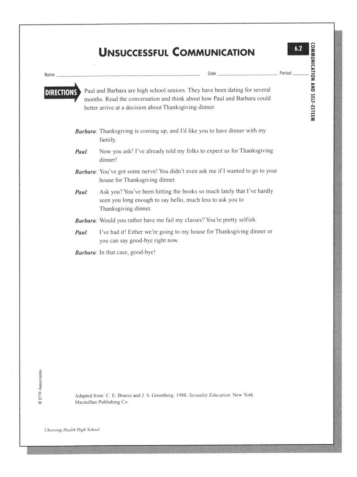

UNSUCCESSFUL COMMUNICATION   6.2

Name _____ Date _____ Period _____

DIRECTIONS Paul and Barbara are high school seniors. They have been dating for several months. Read the conversation and think about how Paul and Barbara could better arrive at a decision about Thanksgiving dinner.

Barbara: Thanksgiving is coming up, and I'd like you to have dinner with my family.

Paul: Now you ask! I've already told my folks to expect us for Thanksgiving dinner!

Barbara: You've got some nerve! You didn't even ask me if I wanted to go to your house for Thanksgiving dinner.

Paul: Ask you? You've been hitting the books so much lately that I've hardly seen you long enough to say hello, much less to ask you to Thanksgiving dinner.

Barbara: Would you rather have me fail my classes? You're pretty selfish.

Paul: I've had it! Either we're going to my house for Thanksgiving dinner or you can say good-bye right now.

Barbara: In that case, good-bye!

Adapted from: C. E. Bruess and J. S. Greenberg. 1988. *Sexuality Education*. New York: Macmillan Publishing Co.

Choosing Health High School

© ETR Associates

COMMUNICATION AND SELF-ESTEEM

2. UNSUCCESSFUL COMMUNICATION

$$\boxed{\text{CONTINUED}}$$

Discuss scenario

Examine the factors with students. Cover the following points:

- Both Paul and Barbara are out to win. Each is trying to get the other to spend Thanksgiving dinner with his or her own family.

- Neither can truly win in this situation, because the only choices they've presented themselves with are to (1) spend the day at Paul's house, (2) spend the day at Barbara's house, or (3) break up their relationship.

- If they decide to spend the day at Barbara's, Paul will have to cancel his plans with his family and put up with the ensuing hassle. He's likely to feel that his wishes are not very important in the relationship, and he's likely to resent being at Barbara's for Thanksgiving.

- If they spend the day at Paul's house, Barbara will be resentful. She might feel that because she asked first, they should go to her house. She also may resent Paul's assumption that he can make plans for both of them without consulting her.

- Someone will be resentful wherever they go, which will probably make Thanksgiving uncomfortable and unenjoyable for all concerned. No matter who wins, both really lose.

- The third possibility—dissolving the relationship—is obviously a no-win solution.

COMMUNITY LINK

Invite a community worker who deals with conflict as a part of the job to speak to the class. Ask the speaker to address the importance of effective communication skills when conflict is an issue. Have the speaker talk about special training that may accompany his or her work.

3. Successful Communication

15–20 minutes
✴

MATERIALS
◆ Successful Communication (6.3)
✴

Students act out scenario
Distribute the **Successful Communication** activity sheet. Ask for volunteers to act out the scenario.

Discuss successful communication
Ask students why this scenario was successful. Use the **Effective Communication** *Instant Expert* to help students identify how the 3 components of successful communication were implemented in the scenario.

Students write about communication
Following the discussion, ask students to describe ways the 3 components of successful communication (active listening, identifying one's position, and brainstorming alternative solutions) were implemented in the scenario. Collect the papers.

(continued...)

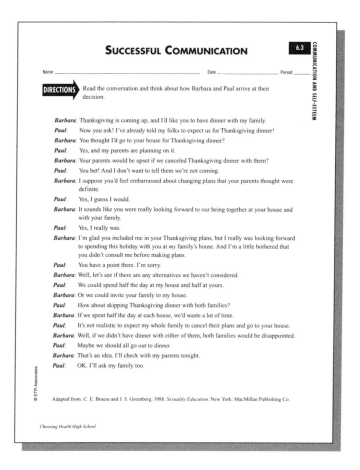

SUCCESSFUL COMMUNICATION 6.3

Name _____ Date _____ Period _____

COMMUNICATION AND SELF-ESTEEM

DIRECTIONS ➤ Read the conversation and think about how Barbara and Paul arrive at their decision.

Barbara: Thanksgiving is coming up, and I'd like you to have dinner with my family.
Paul: Now you ask! I've already told my folks to expect us for Thanksgiving dinner!
Barbara: You thought I'd go to your house for Thanksgiving dinner?
Paul: Yes, and my parents are planning on it.
Barbara: Your parents would be upset if we canceled Thanksgiving dinner with them?
Paul: You bet! And I don't want to tell them we're not coming.
Barbara: I suppose you'd feel embarrassed about changing plans that your parents thought were definite.
Paul: Yes, I guess I would.
Barbara: It sounds like you were really looking forward to our being together at your house and with your family.
Paul: Yes, I really was.
Barbara: I'm glad you included me in your Thanksgiving plans, but I really was looking forward to spending this holiday with you at *my* family's house. And I'm a little bothered that you didn't consult me before making plans.
Paul: You have a point there. I'm sorry.
Barbara: Well, let's see if there are any alternatives we haven't considered.
Paul: We could spend half the day at my house and half at yours.
Barbara: Or we could invite your family to my house.
Paul: How about skipping Thanksgiving dinner with both families?
Barbara: If we spent half the day at each house, we'd waste a lot of time.
Paul: It's not realistic to expect my whole family to cancel their plans and go to your house.
Barbara: Well, if we didn't have dinner with either of them, both families would be disappointed.
Paul: Maybe we should all go out to dinner.
Barbara: That's an idea. I'll check with my parents tonight.
Paul: OK. I'll ask my family too.

© ETR Associates

Adapted from: C. E. Bruess and J. S. Greenberg. 1988. *Sexuality Education*. New York: MacMillan Publishing Co.

Choosing Health High School

3. SUCCESSFUL COMMUNICATION

(CONTINUED)

Ongoing Assessment Look for students' ability to identify the 3 components of successful communication:

- active listening
- identifying one's position
- brainstorming alternative solutions

Barbara's description of the feelings Paul had left unspoken is a demonstration of active listening. She understood that he would be embarrassed by having to cancel Thanksgiving with his family, even though he hadn't explicitly said so.

The scenario demonstrates a win-win solution. Barbara and Paul will suggest a third option to their families. Barbara also knows that Paul now understands her need to be involved in their planning. This successful communication has helped strengthen their relationship and increases their chances of continuing to communicate successfully in the future.

SHARPEN THE SKILL
COMMUNICATION—
DEMONSTRATING SUCCESSFUL COMMUNICATION

Have students identify a conflict and write their own dialogue that demonstrates the 3 components of successful communication.

4. PRACTICING EFFECTIVE COMMUNICATION

15 minutes

Identify problem situations

Ask students to think of situations that could involve communication problems, or use examples such as the following:

- forgetting a birthday or other special event (to demonstrate active listening)
- being late frequently (to demonstrate ways to identify your position)
- a friend who wants to be with other friends all the time instead of being with you (to demonstrate ways to explore alternative solutions)

Dyads practice skills

Divide the class into pairs to practice the 3 components of successful communication (active listening, identifying one's position and exploring alternative solutions). Be sure each student practices each behavior.

5. MEASURING ASSERTIVENESS

Students assess assertiveness

Distribute the **Measure Your Assertiveness** activity sheet and explain the codes. Have students complete the inventory and assess their answers. Ask students how they could become more assertive.

Students respond to situations

Review assertive, nonassertive and aggressive communication, using the **Effective Communication** *Instant Expert* as a guide. Distribute the **What Would You Say?** activity sheet and have students complete it. When students have finished, discuss the differences among the responses.

(continued...)

15 minutes

MATERIALS

♦ Measure Your Assertiveness (6.4)

♦ What Would You Say? (6.5)

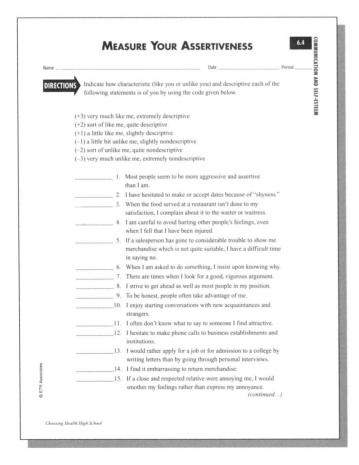

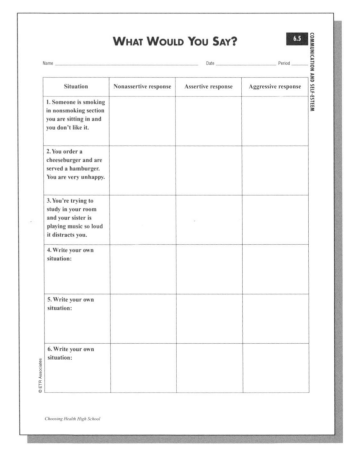

5. Measuring Assertiveness

(CONTINUED)

Groups practice skills

Divide the class into groups of 3 and explain the group assignment:

- Using the situations on the **What Would You Say?** activity sheet, take turns roleplaying assertive, nonassertive and aggressive communication. Two group members should act out the situation, while the third member acts as observer.
- Observers share their comments on the interactions.
- Switch roles.
- Be sure everyone in the group has the opportunity to roleplay each type of behavior and to act as observer.
- Make sure everyone has the opportunity to demonstrate effective communication.

Ongoing Assessment Student roleplays should show:

- level of communication appropriate for the type of message and the receiver
- nonverbal communication consistent with the verbal communication
- evidence of poor communication—failure to listen, an attempt to win, an inability to show an understanding of another's viewpoint, and a rigidity that prevents consideration of alternative solutions
- language system that is understood by the receiver
- use of level 4 communication skills (active listening, identifying one's position and exploring alternative solutions)
- time being set aside for discussion
- use of assertive behavior, if appropriate

EVALUATION

OBJECTIVE 1

Students will be able to:

> **Identify the components of successful communication.**

Review student papers from Activity 3.

CRITERIA

Look for students to identify active listening, identifying one's position and brainstorming as components of successful communication. Allow students to redo and resubmit papers if all 3 components are not present.

OBJECTIVE 2

Students will be able to:

> **Demonstrate effective communication.**

Observe students during the group roleplays in Activity 5 for demonstration of effective communication skills. Allow students to redo and adjust roleplays to demonstrate effective communication.

CRITERIA

Look for:

- level of communication appropriate for the type of message and the receiver
- nonverbal communication consistent with the verbal communication
- evidence of poor communication—failure to listen, an attempt to win, an inability to show an understanding of another's viewpoint, and a rigidity that prevents consideration of alternative solutions
- language system that is understood by the receiver
- use of level 4 communication skills (active listening, identifying one's position and exploring alternative solutions)
- time being set aside for discussion
- use of assertive behavior, if appropriate

EFFECTIVE COMMUNICATION

Health behavior is influenced by various skills. The skill of communicating well can have a positive influence on self-esteem. Poor use of language can contribute to communication problems.

LANGUAGE SYSTEMS

Problems may arise when people do not have the same communication system. They may use different verbal comments, vocal styles or nonverbal behavior. A vivid example of this can be seen when considering the topic of human sexuality.

At least 4 language systems have evolved for communicating about sexuality. They include:

- child language
- street language
- euphemisms
- medical-scientific language

Child Language: Adults have certain terms they often use with young children. Child language might be used to refer to body parts and bodily functions and as terms of endearment. This use of language may lead to children not knowing correct anatomical terms and feeling that such words are inappropriate to use when communicating.

Street Language: As people grow, they learn street language from peers and those who are a little older. These words are often used to shock or to demonstrate knowledge to peers. Street language is also the language of graffiti. This language can be used to impress others, but it is often socially unacceptable.

Euphemisms: Euphemisms make it possible to avoid explicit terms when communicating. They include expressions such as "making love," "sleeping together" and "that time of the month."

Medical-Scientific Language: This language is concrete and technical and includes words such as *penis*, *vagina* and *defecate*.

Awareness of the use and existence of various language systems can help promote better communication. People can develop a wide tolerance for language, try to use the language system of the other person when possible and change language when desirable. People must be sure they are speaking (and understanding) the same language for effective communication to occur.

(continued...)

Effective Communication

CONFLICT RESOLUTION

Successful resolution of conflicts requires high-level (Level 4) communication. At this level, people take some risks, are open to others' input, reveal more of themselves and are honest. High-level communication skills include:

- active or reflective listening
- identifying your position
- exploring alternative solutions or brainstorming

Active or Reflective Listening: Active listening enables us to restate another's words to show we understood her or his meaning. Reflecting the words and thoughts of others shows them that we care enough to really understand their views. Once others receive this caring, they are more willing to listen and understand our viewpoint. The net result is that each speaker not only better understands the other's point of view, but also is less insistent that his or hers is the only valid viewpoint.

Identifying Your Position: Others can more easily understand our position if we can explain our feelings. We may need to ask ourselves, Where am I coming from? Stating thoughts and feelings about a situation helps communication.

Exploring Alternative Solutions or Brainstorming: This step involves first listing all possible solutions without evaluating them. This process allows for creativity without being judgmental. Then these alternatives are evaluated until a solution is reached. Although no one person "wins" with this technique, in actuality everyone wins.

OVERCOMING BARRIERS TO COMMUNICATION

One common barrier to good communication is a failure to set aside time for discussion. In setting up time for discussion, it is wise to make the following plans:

1. Make sure you have plenty of time. Don't be cut short by either of you having to run off somewhere.
2. Don't allow others to interrupt your discussion with phone calls, by barging in on you or with other distractions.
3. Accept all feelings and the verbal expression of these feelings. For example, it is just as appropriate to say "I feel angry when…" as it is to say "I feel terrific when…."
4. Take a risk. Really describe your thoughts and needs. Don't expect the other person to guess what they are.

(continued…)

EFFECTIVE COMMUNICATION

5. Approach the discussion with both of you understanding that the goal is to improve your relationship rather than to see who can shock whom.

6. Expect changes, but not miracles. Communication requires continued work. You might want to seek the help of family members, friends, peer counselors, members of the clergy or others who can contribute to your ability to communicate.

ASSERTIVENESS, NONASSERTIVENESS AND AGGRESSION

The first step in learning to be assertive is to distinguish among assertive, aggressive and nonassertive behaviors.

- *Assertiveness* means standing up for your basic rights without violating someone else's.
- *Aggressiveness* means standing up for your rights (or more) at the expense of someone else's rights.
- *Nonassertiveness* means giving up your basic rights so others can achieve theirs.

The following example helps clarify these distinctions. Suppose you are at a restaurant and you order steak cooked medium. When the steak is brought to your table, you find that the steak is cooked rare.

An aggressive response would be to call the waiter to your table and say in a loud voice, "This isn't cooked! What's the matter with this place? Can't you do anything right? Take this steak back and have it cooked until it's medium!" With this response, you would be ensuring your basic right to have your meat cooked as you ordered it but at the expense of the right of the waiter and cook to make a mistake and be treated politely.

A nonassertive response in this situation would be to say nothing and to eat the rare steak because you don't want to bother the cook or waiter. This response would not violate the rights of the waiter or cook, but would compromise your own right to get the food you order and pay for.

An assertive response would be to call the waiter over to your table and say politely, "I ordered this steak medium and it is not cooked well enough for me. Would you please have it cooked a little longer? Thank you." In this instance, you would be standing up for your own rights while preserving those of the waiter and cook.

(continued...)

EFFECTIVE COMMUNICATION

Body language can also be aggressive, nonassertive or assertive. Aggressive body language includes finger pointing, leaning toward the other person, glaring and a loud, angry tone of voice. Nonassertive body language is characterized by slumped posture, a lack of eye contact, hand-wringing, hesitant speech, whining or laughing nervously, and not saying or doing what you want. Assertive behavior, by contrast, entails sitting or standing tall, looking directly at the person you're talking to, speaking in explicit statements with a steady voice, and making the gestures or physical contact that feel right for you.

While it takes work and conscious attention, communication skills can be improved. Better communication can promote more positive relationships as well as the mental health of the individuals involved.

FINAL EVALUATION

FINAL EVALUATION

Discuss influences on behavior

Distribute The Murder of Crabwell Grommet student reading sheet and have students review it. Discuss how attitudes, knowledge and skills influenced Crabwell Grommet's behavior. Ask students to imagine how the story might have turned out if Crabwell Grommet had felt good about himself and had good communication skills.

Students suggest ways to improve communication

Ask students to think of the things they learned about communication in Units 5 and 6. Have them list ways for Crabwell to improve his communication.

CRITERIA

Look for students to address communication skills in the following areas:

- verbal communication
- nonverbal communication
- types of communication
- language systems
- factors in unsuccessful versus successful communication
- assertive versus aggressive or nonaggressive behavior.

15 minutes

MATERIALS

- classroom set of The Murder of Crabwell Grommet (1.1), from Unit 1

APPENDIXES

Why Comprehensive School Health?

Components of a
Comprehensive Health Program

The Teacher's Role

Teaching Strategies

Glossary

References

WHY COMPREHENSIVE SCHOOL HEALTH?

The quality of life we ultimately achieve is determined in large part by the health decisions we make, the subsequent behaviors we adopt, and the public policies that promote and support the establishment of healthy behaviors.

A healthy student is capable of growing and learning; of producing new knowledge and ideas; of sharing, interacting and living peacefully with others in a complex and changing society. Fostering healthy children is the shared responsibility of families, communities and schools.

Health behaviors, the most important predictors of current and future health status, are influenced by a variety of factors. Factors that lead to and support the establishment of healthy behaviors include:

- awareness and knowledge of health issues
- the skills necessary to practice healthy behaviors
- opportunities to practice healthy behaviors
- support and reinforcement for the practice of healthy behaviors

The perception that a particular healthy behavior is worthwhile often results in young people becoming advocates, encouraging others to adopt the healthy behavior. When these young advocates exert pressure on peers to adopt healthy behaviors, a healthy social norm is established (e.g., tobacco use is unacceptable in this school).

Because health behaviors are learned, they can be shaped and changed. Partnerships between family members, community leaders, teachers and school leaders are a vital key to the initial development and maintenance of children's healthy behaviors and can also play a role in the modification of unhealthy behaviors. Schools, perhaps more than any other single agency in our society, have the opportunity to influence factors that shape the future health and productivity of Americans.

When young people receive reinforcement for the practice of a healthy behavior, they feel good about the healthy behavior. Reinforcement and the subsequent good feeling increase the likelihood that an individual will continue to practice a behavior and thereby establish a positive health habit. The good feeling and the experience of success motivate young people to place a high value on the behavior (e.g., being a nonsmoker is good).

From *Step by Step to Comprehensive School Health,* W. M. Kane (Santa Cruz, CA: ETR Associates, 1992).

COMPONENTS OF A COMPREHENSIVE HEALTH PROGRAM

The school's role in fostering the development of healthy students involves more than providing classes in health. There are 8 components of a comprehensive health education program:

- **School Health Instruction**—Instruction is the in-class aspect of the program. As in other subject areas, a scope of content defines the field. Application of classroom instruction to real life situations is critical.

- **Healthy School Environment**—The school environment includes both the physical and psychological surroundings of students, faculty and staff. The physical environment should be free of hazards; the psychological environment should foster healthy development.

- **School Health Services**—School health services offer a variety of activities that address the health status of students and staff.

- **Physical Education and Fitness**—Participation in physical education and fitness activities promotes healthy development. Students need information about how and why to be active and encouragement to develop skills that will contribute to fitness throughout their lives.

- **School Nutrition and Food Services**—The school's nutritional program provides an excellent opportunity to model healthy behaviors. Schools that provide healthy food choices and discourage availability of unhealthy foods send a clear message to students about the importance of good nutrition.

- **School-Based Counseling and Personal Support**—School counseling and support services play an important role in responding to special needs and providing personal support for individual students, teachers and staff. These services can also provide programs that promote schoolwide mental, emotional and social well-being.

- **Schoolsite Health Promotion**—Health promotion is a combination of educational, organizational and environmental activities designed to encourage students and staff to adopt healthier lifestyles and become better consumers of health care services. It views the school and its activities as a total environment.

- **School, Family and Community Health Promotion Partnerships**— Partnerships that unite schools, families and communities can address communitywide issues. These collaborative partnerships are the cornerstone of health promotion and disease prevention.

THE TEACHER'S ROLE

The teacher plays a critical role in meeting the challenge to empower students with the knowledge, skills and ability to make healthy behavior choices throughout their lives.

Instruction

Teachers need to provide students with learning opportunities that go beyond knowledge. Instruction must include the chance to practice skills that will help students make healthy decisions.

Involve Families and Communities

The issues in health are real-life issues, issues that families and communities deal with daily. Students need to see the relationship of what they learn at school to what occurs in their homes and their communities.

Model Healthy Behavior

Teachers educate students by their actions too. Students watch the way teachers manage health issues in their own lives. Teachers need to ask themselves if they are modeling the health behaviors they want students to adopt.

Maintain a Healthy Environment

The classroom environment has both physical and emotional aspects. It is the teacher's role to maintain a safe physical environment. It is also critical to provide an environment that is sensitive, respectful and developmentally appropriate.

Establish Groundrules

It is very important to establish classroom groundrules before discussing sensitive topics or issues. Setting and consistently enforcing groundrules establishes an atmosphere of respect, in which students can share and explore their personal thoughts, feelings, opinions and values.

Refer Students to Appropriate Services

Teachers may be the first to notice illness, learning disorders or emotional distress in students. The role of the teacher is one of referral. Most districts have guidelines for teachers to follow.

Legal Compliance

Teachers must make every effort to communicate to parents and other family members about the nature of the curriculum. Instruction about certain topics, such as sexuality, HIV or drug use, often must follow notification guidelines regulated by state law. Most states also require teachers to report any suspected cases of child abuse or neglect.

TEACHING STRATEGIES

The resource books incorporate a variety of instructional strategies. This variety is essential in addressing the needs of different kinds of learners. Different strategies are grouped according to their general education purpose. When sequenced, these strategies are designed to help students acquire the knowledge and skills they need to choose healthy behavior. Strategies are identified with each activity. Some strategies are traditional, while others are more interactive, encouraging students to help each other learn.

The strategies are divided into 4 categories according to their general purpose:

- providing key information
- encouraging creative expression
- sharing thoughts, feelings and opinions
- developing critical thinking

The following list details strategies in each category.

Providing Key Information

Information provides the foundation for learning. Before students can move to higher-level thinking, they need to have information about a topic. In lieu of a textbook, this series uses a variety of strategies to provide students the information they need to take actions for their health.

Anonymous Question Box

An anonymous question box provides the opportunity for all students to get answers to questions they might be hesitant to ask in class. It also gives teachers time to think about answers to difficult questions or to look for more information.

Questions should be reviewed and responded to regularly, and all questions placed in the box should be taken seriously. If you don't know the answer to a question, research it and report back to students.

You may feel that some questions would be better answered privately. Offer students the option of signing their questions if they want a private, written answer. Any questions not answered in class can then be answered privately.

Current Events

Analyzing local, state, national and international current events helps students relate classroom discussion to everyday life. It also helps students understand how local, national and global events and policies affect health status. Resources for current

TEACHING STRATEGIES

events include newspapers, magazines and other periodicals, radio and television programs and news.

Demonstrations and Experiments

Teachers, guest speakers or students can use demonstrations and experiments to show how something works or why something is important. These activities also provide a way to show the correct process for doing something, such as a first-aid procedure.

Demonstrations and experiments should be carefully planned and conducted. They often involve the use of supporting materials.

Games and Puzzles

Games and puzzles can be used to provide a different environment in which learning can take place. They are frequently amusing and sometimes competitive.

Many types of games and puzzles can be adapted to present and review health concepts. It may be a simple question-and-answer game or an adaptation of games such as Bingo, Concentration or Jeopardy. Puzzles include crosswords and word searches.

A game is played according to a specific set of rules. Game rules should be clear and simple. Using groups of students in teams rather than individual contestants helps involve the entire class.

Guest Speakers

Guest speakers can be recruited from students' families, the school and the community. They provide a valuable link between the classroom and the "real world."

Speakers should be screened before being invited to present to the class. They should have some awareness of the level of student knowledge and should be given direction for the content and focus of the presentation.

Interviewing

Students can interview experts and others about a specific topic either inside or outside of class. Invite experts, family members and others to visit class, or ask students to interview others (family members or friends) outside of class.

Advance preparation for an organized interview session increases the learning potential. A brainstorming session before the interview allows students to develop questions to ask during the interview.

TEACHING STRATEGIES

Oral Presentations

Individual students or groups or panels of students can present information orally to the rest of the class. Such presentations may sometimes involve the use of charts or posters to augment the presentation.

Students enjoy learning and hearing from each other, and the experience stimulates positive interaction. It also helps build students' communication skills.

Encouraging Creative Expression

Student creativity should be encouraged and challenged. Creative expression provides the opportunity to integrate language arts, fine arts and personal experience into a lesson. It also helps meet the diverse needs of students with different learning styles.

Artistic Expression or Creative Writing

Students may be offered a choice of expressing themselves in art or through writing. They may write short stories, poems or letters, or create pictures or collages about topics they are studying. Such a choice accommodates the differing needs and talents of students.

This technique can be used as a follow-up to most lessons. Completed work should be displayed in the classroom, at school or in the community.

Dramatic Presentations

Dramatic presentations may take the form of skits or mock news, radio or television shows. They can be presented to the class or to larger groups in the school or community. When equipment is available, videotapes of these presentations provide an opportunity to present students' work to other classes in the school and other groups in the community.

Such presentations are highly motivating activities, because they actively involve students in learning desired concepts. They also allow students to practice new behaviors in a safe setting and help them personalize information presented in class.

Roleplays

Acting out difficult situations provides students practice in new behaviors in a safe setting. Sometimes students are given a part to play, and other times they are given an idea and asked to improvise. Students need time to decide the central action of the

TEACHING STRATEGIES

situation and how they will resolve it before they make their presentation. Such activities are highly motivating because they actively involve students in learning desired concepts or practicing certain behaviors.

Sharing Thoughts, Feelings and Opinions

In the sensitive areas of health education, students may have a variety of opinions and feelings. Providing a safe atmosphere in which to discuss opinions and feelings encourages students to share their ideas and listen and learn from others. Such discussion also provides an opportunity to clarify misinformation and correct misconceptions.

Brainstorming

Brainstorming is used to stimulate discussion of an issue or topic. It can be done with the whole class or in smaller groups. It can be used both to gather information and to share thoughts and opinions.

All statements should be accepted without comment or judgment from the teacher or other students. Ideas can be listed on the board, on butcher paper or newsprint or on a transparency. Brainstorming should continue until all ideas have been exhausted or a predetermined time limit has been reached.

Class Discussion

A class discussion led by the teacher or by students is a valuable educational strategy. It can be used to initiate, amplify or summarize a lesson. Such discussions also provide a way to share ideas, opinions and concerns that may have been generated in small group work.

Clustering

Clustering is a simple visual technique that involves diagraming ideas around a main topic. The main topic is written on the board and circled. Other related ideas are then attached to the central idea or to each other with connecting lines.

Clustering can be used as an adjunct to brainstorming. Because there is no predetermined number of secondary ideas, clustering can accommodate all brainstorming ideas.

Continuum Voting

Continuum voting is a stimulating discussion technique. Students express the extent to which they agree or disagree with a statement read by the teacher. The classroom should be prepared for this activity with a sign that says "Agree" on one wall and a sign that says "Disagree" on the opposite wall. There should be room for students to move freely between the 2 signs.

As the teacher reads a statement, students move to a point between the signs that reflects their thoughts or feelings. The closer to the "Agree" sign they stand, the stronger their agreement. The closer to the "Disagree" sign they stand, the stronger their disagreement. A position in the center between the signs indicates a neutral stance.

Dyad Discussion

Working in pairs allows students to provide encouragement and support to each other. Students who may feel uncomfortable sharing in the full class may be more willing to share their thoughts and feelings with 1 other person. Depending on the task, dyads may be temporary, or students may meet regularly with a partner and work together to achieve their goals.

Forced Field Analysis

This strategy is used to discuss an issue that is open to debate. Students analyze a situation likely to be approved by some students and opposed by others. For example, if the subject of discussion was the American diet, some students might support the notion that Americans consume healthy foods because of the wide variety of foods available. Other students might express concern about the amount of foods that are high in sodium, fat and sugar.

Questioning skills are critical to the success of this technique. A good way to open such a discussion is to ask students, "What questions should you ask to determine if you support or oppose this idea?" The pros and cons of students' analysis can be charted on the board or on a transparency.

Journal Writing

Journal writing affords the opportunity for thinking and writing. Expressive writing requires that students become actively involved in the learning process. However, writing may become a less effective tool for learning if students must worry about spelling and punctuation. Students should be encouraged to write freely in their journals, without fear of evaluation.

Panel Discussion

Panel discussions provide an opportunity to discuss different points of view about a health topic, problem or issue. Students can research and develop supporting arguments for different sides. Such research and discussion enhances understanding of content.

Panel members may include experts from the community as well as students. Panel discussions are usually directed by a moderator and may be followed by a question and answer period.

Self-Assessment

Personal inventories provide a tool for self-assessment. Providing privacy around personal assessments allows students to be honest in their responses. Volunteers can share answers or the questions can be discussed in general, but no students should have to share answers they would prefer to keep private. Students can use the information to set personal goals for changing behaviors.

Small Groups

Students working together can help stimulate each other's creativity. Small group activities are cooperative, but have less formal structure than cooperative learning groups. These activities encourage collective thinking and provide opportunities for students to work with others and increase social skills.

Surveys and Inventories

Surveys and inventories can be used to assess knowledge, attitudes, beliefs and practices. These instruments can be used to gather knowledge about a variety of groups, including students, parents and other family members, and teachers.

Students can use surveys others have designed or design their own. When computers are available, students can use them to summarize their information, create graphs and prepare presentations of the data.

Developing Critical Thinking

Critical thinking skills help students analyze health topics and issues. These activities require that students learn to gather information, consider the consequences of actions and behaviors and make responsible decisions. They challenge students to perform higher-level thinking and clearly communicate their ideas.

Case Studies

Case studies provide written histories of a problem or situation. Students can read, discuss and analyze these situations. This strategy encourages student involvement and helps students personalize the health-related concepts presented in class.

TEACHING STRATEGIES

Cooperative Learning Groups

Cooperative learning is an effective teaching strategy that has been shown to have a positive effect on students' achievement and interpersonal skills. Students can work in small groups to disseminate and share information, analyze ideas or solve problems. The size of the group depends on the nature of the lesson and the make-up of the class. Groups work best with from 2–6 members.

Group structure will affect the success of the lessons. Groups can be formed by student choice, random selection, or a more formal, teacher-influenced process. Groups seem to function best when they represent the variety and balance found in the classroom. Groups also work better when each student has a responsibility within the group (reader, recorder, timer, reporter, etc.).

While groups are working on their tasks, the teacher should move from group to group, answering questions and dealing with any problems that arise. At the conclusion of the group process, some closure should take place.

Debates

Students can debate the pros and cons of many issues relating to health. Suggesting that students defend an opposing point of view provides an additional learning experience.

During a debate, each side has the opportunity to present their arguments and to refute each others' arguments. After the debate, class members can choose the side with which they agree.

Factual Writing

Once students have been presented with information about a topic, a variety of writing assignments can challenge them to clarify and express their ideas and opinions. Position papers, letters to the editor, proposals and public service announcements provide a forum in which students can express their opinions, supporting them with facts, figures and reasons.

Media Analysis

Students can analyze materials from a variety of media, including printed matter, music, TV programs, movies, video games and advertisements, to identify health-related messages. Such analysis might include identifying the purpose of the piece, the target audience, underlying messages, motivations and stereotypes.

TEACHING STRATEGIES

Personal Contracts

Personal contracts, individual commitments to changing behavior, can help students make positive changes in their health-related behaviors. The wording of a personal contract may include the behavior to be changed, a plan for changing the behavior and the identification of possible problems and support systems.

However, personal contracts should be used with caution. Behavior change may be difficult, especially in the short term. Students should be encouraged to make personal contracts around goals they are likely to meet.

Research

Research requires students to seek information to complete a task. Students may be given prepared materials that they must use to complete an assignment, or they may have to locate resources and gather information on their own. As part of this strategy, students must compile and organize the information they collect.

GLOSSARY

A

abstract—Not concrete; thought of apart from any material objects.

active listening—Restating another's words to show that the meaning has been understood.

affirmation—Positive declaration or assertion.

aggressive communication—Standing up for your rights at the expense of someone else's rights.

assertive communication—Standing up for your basic rights without violating someone else's.

attitude—State of mind or opinion.

B

barrier—Obstruction; something that hinders.

benefit—Anything contributing to an improvement in condition; advantage; help.

body language—A form of nonverbal communication made up of facial expressions, body movement, posture, gestures, etc., that are clues to a person's thoughts and feelings. Sometimes body language can speak louder than words.

brainstorming—Listing all possible ideas, without judging or eliminating any.

C

challenge—Anything that calls for special effort or dedication.

communication—The ability to express thoughts, feelings and reactions and to exchange information among people through a common system of symbols, signs or behaviors; involves both a sender and a receiver.

communication barrier—Anything which hinders clear communication between the sender and the receiver of a message; any type of interference that can confuse the meaning of the message being sent.

condition—Manner or state of being.

confidence—A belief in one's own competence; assurance.

consensus—General agreement within a group concerning a certain idea.

culture—Ideas, customs, skills and arts of a people or group; collection of shared practices, rules and values of a group.

D

decision—The act of making up one's mind; a judgment or conclusion.

disclosure—Revealing one's true thoughts and feelings to another.

distress—A negative response to stress.

dynamic—Constantly changing.

GLOSSARY

E

emotional response—The feeling a person experiences as a reaction to a situation or event.

euphemism—A less direct word or phrase, usually used in regard to a sensitive topic.

F

facial expression—How the features of the face respond to emotions; a nonverbal gesture or clue which can convey how a person feels or thinks about a certain topic, idea or emotion. One aspect of body language.

failure—The state of not succeeding in doing or becoming something.

friend—A person one knows well and is fond of.

friendship—Attachment between people who know each other well.

G

goal—An end that a person aims to reach or accomplish.

H

habit—An act that is done often, in a certain way, and has become automatic.

health—Well-being in all dimensions of life including mental, emotional, social and physical.

I

ideal—Thought of as perfect or a perfect model.

individuality—The sum of the characteristics that set a person or thing apart.

influence—The ability of a person or thing to affect others.

introspection—Looking into one's own mind, feelings, etc.

L

language—Human speech and its written symbols; a means of communicating.

language system—The particular style of verbal expression characteristic of a person, group, profession, etc.

M

media—Means of communication, such as newspapers, radio and TV, that provide information to the public.

mental health—The ability to recognize reality and cope with life situations.

GLOSSARY

N

negative self-talk—Communication with oneself that diminishes or denies one's good qualities.

nonassertive communication—Giving up your basic rights so others can achieve theirs.

nonverbal communication—The use of symbols, signs or body language to convey a message.

O

1-way verbal communication—Information is passed by one person to another with no opportunity for the receiver to provide feedback of any kind.

opportunity—A useful chance or occasion for something positive.

overcoming barriers—Learning a new skill to replace a behavior which interferes with communication.

P

personality—Unique constellation of emotions, thoughts and behaviors that determine who a person is and how each person functions and adapts to life.

positive self-talk—Communication with oneself that affirms or celebrates one's good qualities.

R

realistic—Tending to face facts; practical.

roadblock—Any hindrance or obstacle in the way of an objective.

S

satisfaction—The state of being content, fulfilled, etc.

self-actualization—Fulfilling one's human potential along with one's basic needs.

self-esteem—Measure of how much a person values himself or herself.

self-image—A person's perceptions and opinions about himself or herself.

self-worth—An individual's measure of how much he or she is valued.

socially acceptable—Adequate enough to satisfy a standard; satisfactory; appropriate.

stress—The feeling of being under pressure; bodily wear and tear caused by physical or psychological arousal by outside events.

stressor—Anything that triggers a stress response (e.g., external events, internal reactions).

success—A favorable or satisfactory outcome or result.

sympathy—Mutual liking or understanding.

GLOSSARY

T

tactile communication—Nonverbal communication received through the sense of touch.

2-way verbal communication—The process of passing information between speaker and listener with limited feedback.

U

unique—One of a kind; different from all others.

V

verbal communication—Transferring information, thoughts or feelings from one person to another by talking.

visual communication—Transferring information, thoughts or feelings from one person to another using the sense of sight.

REFERENCES

Bruess, C. E., and J. S. Greenberg. 1994. *Sexuality education: Theory and practice.* 3d ed. Dubuque, IA: Brown and Benchmark.

Bruess, C. E., and G. Richardson. 1995. *Decisions for health.* 4th ed. Dubuque, IA: Brown and Benchmark.

Cinelli, B., L. J. Bechtel, M. Rose-Colley and R. Nye. 1995. Critical thinking skills in health education. *Journal of Health Education* 26 (2): 119-120.

Dalis, G. T. 1994. Effective health instruction: Both a science and an art. *Journal of Health Education* 24 (5): 289-294.

de Gaston, J. F., L. Jensen and S. Weed. 1995. A closer look at adolescent sexual activity. *Journal of Youth and Adolescence* 24 (4): 465-479.

Greenberg, J. 1989. *Health education: Learner-centered instructional strategies.* Dubuque, IA: William C. Brown Co.

Greenberg, J., and R. Gold. 1994. *Holt health.* New York: Holt, Rinehart and Winston.

Kahn, L., C. W. Warren, W. A. Harris, J. L. Collins, K. A. Douglas, M. E. Collins, B. I. Williams, J. G. Ross and L. J. Kolbe. 1995. Youth risk behavior surveillance. *Journal of School Health* 65 (5): 163-171.

Klein, H. A. 1995. Self-perception in late adolescence: An interactive perspective. *Adolescence* 30 (119): 539-548.

O'Brien, W. H., L. VanEgeren and P. B. Mumby. 1995. Predicting health behaviors using measures of optimism and perceived risk. *Health Values* 19 (1): 21-28.

Paterson, J., J. Pryor and J. Field. 1995. Adolescent attachment to parents and friends in relation to aspects of self-esteem. *Journal of Youth and Adolescence* 24 (3): 365-376.

Prochaska, J. O., J. C. Norcross and C. C. DiClemente. 1994. *Changing for good.* New York: William Morrow.

Strecher, V. J., G. H. Seijts, G. J. Kok, G. P. Latham, R. Glasgow, B. DeVellis, R. M. Meertens and D. W. Bulger. 1995. Goal setting as a strategy for health behavior change. *Health Education Quarterly* 22 (2): 190-200.

Torres, R., F. Fernandez and D. Maceira. 1995. Self-esteem and value of health as correlates of adolescent health behavior. *Adolescence* 30 (118): 403-412.

CONTENTS

1.1 The Murder of Crabwell Grommet

1.2 Health Habit to Change

1.3 Health Habit to Change Example

2.1 Self-Esteem and Mental Health

2.2 Name Portrait

2.3 Name Portrait Example

2.4 Characteristics of Mental Health

3.1 Self-Esteem Assessment

3.2 Self-Esteem Log

4.1 Problem-Solving Steps

4.2 Problem-Solving Skills

4.3 Decision Tree Example

4.4 Decision Tree

4.5 Decision-Making Dilemmas

5.1 Types of Communication

5.2 What Do You See? (1)

5.3 What Do You See? (2)

5.4 What Do You See? (3)

6.1 The Communication Gap

6.2 Unsuccessful Communication

6.3 Successful Communication

6.4 Measure Your Assertiveness

6.5 What Would You Say?

THE MURDER OF CRABWELL GROMMET

STUDENT READING

On the morning of his 42nd birthday, Crabwell Grommet awoke to a peal of particularly ominous thunder. Glancing with bleary eyes out the window, he saw written in fiery letters across the sky:

Someone is trying to kill you, Crabwell Grommet.

With shaking hands, Grommet lit his first cigarette of the day. He didn't question the message. You didn't question messages like that. His only question was Who?

At breakfast, he salted his fried eggs as he told his wife, Gratia, "Someone is trying to kill me."

"Who?" she asked with horror.

Grommet slowly stirred the cream and sugar into his coffee and shook his head. "I don't know," he said.

Convinced though he was, Grommet didn't go to the police with such a story. He decided his only course was to go about his daily routine and hope somehow to outwit his would-be murderer. He tried to think during the drive to his office. But the frustration of making time by beating lights and switching lanes occupied him wholly. Nor, once behind his desk, could he find a moment, what with jangling phones, urgent memos and the problems and decisions piling up as they did each day.

It wasn't until his second martini at lunch that the full terror of his position struck him. It was all he could do to finish his lasagna.

"I can't panic," he said to himself, lighting his cigar. "I simply must live my life as usual."

So he worked until 7 as usual. Drove home fast as usual. Ate a hearty dinner as usual. Studied business reports as usual and took his usual 2 sleeping pills in order to get his usual 6 hours' sleep.

As the days passed, he stuck to his routine. And as the months went by, he began to take a perverse pleasure in his ability to survive.

"Whoever's trying to get me," he'd say to his wife, "hasn't got me yet. I'm too smart for him."

"Oh, please be careful," she'd reply, ladling him a second helping of beef stroganoff.

The pride grew as he managed to go on living for years. But death came at last to Crabwell Grommet. It came at his desk on a particularly busy day. He was 51.

His grief-stricken widow demanded a full autopsy.

The autopsy showed only emphysema, arteriosclerosis, duodenal ulcers, cirrhosis of the liver, cardiac necrosis, a cerebrovascular aneurysm, pulmonary edema, obesity, circulatory problems and a touch of lung cancer. "How glad Crabwell would have been to know," his widow said, smiling proudly through her tears, "that he died of natural causes."

HEALTH HABIT TO CHANGE

Name _____ Date _____ Period _____

DIRECTIONS ▶ Describe 1 habit related to health you think you would like to change. Then answer the questions about the change.

1. What habit would you like to change?

2. Describe how this habit is related to health.

3. How is the habit influenced by social pressure?

4. How is the habit influenced by habits?

5. How is the habit influenced by your attitudes and values?

6. How is the habit influenced by what you know?

7. Which of the above influences has the most impact on you?

8. How could you make a change?

HEALTH HABIT TO CHANGE EXAMPLE

 **DIRECTIONS** Describe 1 habit related to health you think you would like to change. Then answer the questions about the change.

1. What habit would you like to change?
   I would like to change an eating habit. I would like to eat more vegetables and cut down on fat.

2. Describe how this habit is related to health.
   People need 3–4 servings of vegetables every day for good nutrition. I rarely ever eat 2 servings a day. And you don't really need much fatty food. I eat fries and a shake almost every day. They have lots of fat.

3. How is the habit influenced by social pressure?
   I eat out with my friends at places that mainly serve fast foods. They eat fries, so I eat fries and a shake.

4. How is the habit influenced by habits?
   My habit is not to eat lunch, so I'm really hungry after school.

5. How is the habit influenced by your attitudes and values?
   It is not really cool to eat salad with my friends. I like fries and shakes. Plus I'm really hungry after school.

6. How is the habit influenced by what you know?
   I know I should eat a salad instead of fries but I don't. Now I'm concerned. That's why I want to change.

7. Which of the above influences has the most impact on you?
   The social influence is the strongest. I want to be accepted and do what my friends do.

8. How could you make a change?
   I could eat lunch so I won't be hungry after school. If I snack on something healthy like carrot sticks and fresh broccoli, I'll be eating more vegetables.

SELF-ESTEEM AND MENTAL HEALTH

STUDENT READING

SELF-ESTEEM

People are not born with an idea that they are good or bad, smart or stupid, pretty or ugly, lovable or unlovable. They develop these ideas through contact with significant people in their lives. Our self-image or picture of ourselves, is based on input from families, teachers and peers.

Self-image is what a person perceives and believes about himself or herself. The attitudes and values that affect self-image, and the judgments a person makes about it, form that person's self-esteem. Self-esteem indicates how capable, significant, successful and worthy people believe themselves to be.

When people think about themselves, they are really thinking about all of the qualities that make them an individual, including personal values, goals, abilities, worth, physical appearance and purpose in life. Self-esteem is also influenced by what people believe others think of them.

Some people have positive or high self-esteem. They are generally satisfied with who they are and what they are doing with their lives. Other people have negative or low self-esteem. They are not very satisfied with who they are or what they are doing. Some people's self-esteem falls somewhere in between. They may not be sure how they feel about themselves.

Self-esteem can change. A person with positive self-esteem may sometimes have negative self-esteem or vice-versa.

WHY IS SELF-ESTEEM IMPORTANT?

Self-esteem has a large effect on people's behavior. Behavior is usually linked to how people feel about themselves. For example, if you believe you can be successful at many things you try, chances are you will try more and more things—and get better at doing them.

Positive self-esteem helps increase motivation and encourages learning. It helps people succeed in their relationships and careers. People who do not have positive self-esteem may feel unworthy,

inadequate, helpless, inferior, or that they can't improve their lives. People with negative self-esteem often feel they will fail.

MENTAL HEALTH

Mental health measures how well a person is able to cope with life's events, grow emotionally, and develop to the fullest potential. Positive mental health means feeling good about yourself. This includes accepting how you look, being content with life, and having inner peace. It also means a person actively seeks new experiences and challenges.

People with positive mental health enjoy many different interests and activities. They tend to use good judgment and think clearly. They are self-disciplined in their thinking and actions. They like other people. Like everyone else, they have problems. But they know that coping with problems is part of life.

People with poor mental health are more likely to have conflicting feelings about their lives. They often don't think ahead or follow through on things. They may do things to discourage friendships or good relations with others (such as provoking people). They may not even be aware they are doing this. They may find it hard to see beyond their own wants and needs.

SELF-ACTUALIZATION

Self-actualization is a term that means a person has positive self-esteem and mental health. People who are self-actualized have come to terms with their own place in the world. They seem to have a purpose outside themselves or be involved in a cause they really care about. They are comfortable with themselves and their lives. A self-actualized person has reached a very high level of mental health.

Being self-actualized means taking responsibility for looking at yourself and being honest. It demands awareness. It means you move toward realizing your full potential.

Name Portrait

Name _____ Date _____ Period _____

 **DIRECTIONS** For each letter in your first name, write a word that describes 1 of your positive attributes. Then decorate your name portrait.

Name Portrait Example

 **DIRECTIONS** For each letter in your first name, write a word that describes 1 of your positive attributes. Then decorate your name portrait.

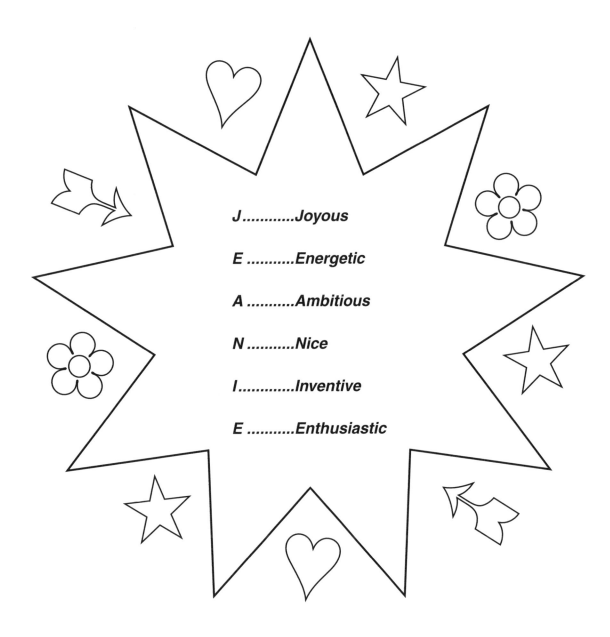

J............Joyous

E ....Energetic

A ....Ambitious

N ....Nice

I.............Inventive

E ....Enthusiastic

Comprehensive Health for High School

CHARACTERISTICS OF MENTAL HEALTH

STUDENT READING

MENTALLY HEALTHY PEOPLE:

★ Are able and willing to assume responsibilities that fit their age.

★ *Participate with pleasure in the experiences of each stage of life. They don't hold on to earlier periods or spend their time looking ahead to a later period.*

★ Willingly accept the experiences and responsibilities of their role or position in life, even though they may object to the role or position.

★ *Attack problems that require solutions, rather than finding ways to evade them.*

★ Enjoy overcoming obstacles to personal growth and happiness, once they are sure that the obstacles are real and not imaginary.

★ *Make decisions with a minimum of worry, conflict, advice seeking, or other forms of running away.*

★ Stick with their choices, until new factors of crucial importance enter the picture.

★ *Find major satisfaction in actual accomplishments and experiences, rather than in wishful thinking.*

★ Know that thinking is a blueprint for action, not a way to delay or escape action.

★ *Learn from defeats instead of finding excuses for them.*

★ Don't make successes bigger than they really are, or think past successes will apply in different areas.

★ *Know how to work when working and how to play when playing.*

★ Say no to situations that are not in their best interest in the long run, even though these situations may give temporary satisfaction.

★ *Say yes to situations that will ultimately help them, even though these situations may be unpleasant right now.*

★ Can show anger directly when injured. Can defend their rights with action that fits the kind and amount of the injury.

★ *Show affection directly and in ways that fit the situation.*

★ Can endure pain and frustration if it is not in their power to alter the cause.

★ *Have their habits and mental attitudes well organized so that they can quickly make changes called for by the difficulties they meet.*

★ Can focus their energy on a single goal they really want to achieve.

★ *Do not try to change the fact that life is an endless struggle. They know that people who don't fight themselves will have more strength and the best judgment for the outside battle.*

★ Can develop and maintain family and other intimate relationships.

SELF-ESTEEM ASSESSMENT

Name _____ Date _____ Period _____

DIRECTIONS➤ Indicate whether or not each item describes you by circling "a" or "b."

a = describes me   b = does not describe me

1. People generally like me.   a   b   ☐

2. I am comfortable talking in class.   a   b   ☐

3. I like to do new things.   a   b   ☐

4. I give in very easily.   a   b   ☐

5. I'm a failure.   a   b   ☐

6. I'm shy.   a   b   ☐

7. I have trouble making up my mind.   a   b   ☐

8. I am popular with people at school.   a   b   ☐

9. My life is all mixed up.   a   b   ☐

10. I often feel upset at home.   a   b   ☐

11. I often wish I were someone else.   a   b   ☐

12. I often worry.   a   b   ☐

13. I can be depended on.   a   b   ☐

14. I often express my views.   a   b   ☐

15. I think I am doing OK with my life.   a   b   ☐

16. I feel good about what I have accomplished recently.   a   b   ☐

Total ☐

(continued...)

From C. E. Bruess and G. Richardson. 1995. *Decisions for Health.* 4th ed. Dubuque, IA: Brown and Benchmark.

© ETR Associates

Choosing Health High School

SELF-ESTEEM ASSESSMENT

CONTINUED

SCORING

DIRECTIONS Determine how many matches you have with the following key. Put a ✓ mark in the box when you have a match and then count the number of matches and record in the large box marked *Total*.

1. a	5. b	9. b	13. a
2. a	6. b	10. b	14. a
3. a	7. b	11. b	15. a
4. b	8. a	12. b	16. a

INTERPRETATION

12–16   high self-esteem

8–11   moderately high self-esteem

4–7   moderately low self-esteem

0–3   low self-esteem

Remember, self-esteem is always changing. We influence it by our own behavior and the ways we look at ourselves. The important thing is to try to move toward the positive.

SELF-ESTEEM LOG

Name _____ Date _____ Period _____

DIRECTIONS ➤ List ways you can increase your positive self-esteem. Then, for 3 days, describe what you do related to each way.

Ways to increase my self-esteem:	How I did this:			Total number of times I did this	How effective was this action?
	Day 1	Day 2	Day 3		
1.					
2.					
3.					
4.					

Choosing Health High School

PROBLEM-SOLVING STEPS

1. Recognize the problem.

2. Own the problem.

3. Break the problem into smaller parts.

4. Gather information.

5. Formulate trial solutions.

6. Act now.

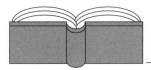

PROBLEM-SOLVING SKILLS

STUDENT READING

A simple and effective problem-solving process includes these 6 steps:

1. Recognize the problem.
2. Own the problem.
3. Break the problem into smaller parts.
4. Gather information.
5. Formulate trial solutions.
6. Act now.

• **Recognize the problem.** Recognizing the problem is an important first step. Not admitting there is a problem or just hoping it will go away usually won't work. For example, people who drink alcohol or smoke cigarettes may recognize the need to quit when they see friends quit, read an article on the dangers of smoking or drinking, or begin to feel negative physical effects.

To make the best decision, define the issue to be resolved or the goal to be reached as clearly as possible. For example, does "drinking" include beer and caffeine drinks? Does "smoking" mean marijuana as well as tobacco?

• **Own the problem.** This step is often ignored. We need to realize that we are responsible for our own happiness or unhappiness. It may be easy to blame others for our problem—and sometimes they might contribute to it. But we need to be in charge of our lives and be able to make our own decisions.

• **Break the problem into smaller parts.** Smaller pieces are easier to deal with. For example, it might make sense to focus on the noise level in our own neighborhood first instead of trying to influence pollution levels throughout the city. Later, there may be ways to deal with the bigger parts of the problem.

• **Gather information.** Gathering information about the problem is an important step. It might mean reading articles, talking to experts, going to meetings or workshops, or asking for others' opinions.

• **Formulate trial solutions.** Begin by thinking of as many solutions as possible. Don't stop to judge them. This is called brainstorming.

Then these trial solutions should be carefully evaluated. Do they agree with our values and goals? Are they realistic and possible? How much cost (time, money, effort, etc.) might be involved? Is it worth it to us? What consequences might result from various solutions? Answering these and other related questions will help eliminate some solutions. Then we can focus on the best ones and choose one to try.

• **Act now.** Then it is time to act. Often people will go through the earlier decision-making steps, but fail to take action. Decisions can only be made realities through action. It doesn't help to come this far and then do nothing.

If a solution is tried and doesn't seem to work, it is OK to try a second or even a third solution. If none of the "best" solutions work out, we might need to go back and come up with more trial solutions (Step 5) or even seek more information (Step 4). Evaluating the process and the outcome helps us make better decisions in the future.

DECISION TREE EXAMPLE

Deciding to not use alcohol at a party

Invited to party where there will be alcohol

- **Don't go to party**
  - **Make an excuse**
    - Say you feel ill and can't go
    - Say your parent(s) won't let you go
  - **Condemn alcohol**
    - Say you won't go to a party where alcohol is present
    - Say you don't like people who drink alcohol
  - **Do something else with friends who don't drink**
    - Plan a party without alcohol
    - Go to a movie instead of the party
- **Go but don't drink alcohol**
  - **Drink other beverages**
    - Promote the benefits of not drinking alcohol
    - Say nothing about alcohol
  - **Avoid drinkers at party**
    - Plan activities only with those who don't drink alcohol
    - Tell those drinking alcohol that you don't want to be with them
  - **Pretend to drink alcohol**
    - Spend time with those drinking alcohol
    - Stay away from the alcohol drinkers

DECISION TREE

Name _____ Date _____ Period _____

DECISION-MAKING DILEMMAS

Name _____ Date _____ Period _____

A FRIEND'S PROBLEM

You have a friend who is very smart and has lots of positive traits. But your friend is unhappy, has negative self-esteem and doesn't feel that life is fair. Your friend recognizes this is a problem and has asked you for suggestions on how to feel better. Using a decision tree, what kinds of choices might you suggest?

A NEW RELATIONSHIP

You have been dating someone for 6 weeks and find him or her interesting and enjoyable. You feel the relationship is off to a great start. But this person is now pressuring you to participate in more intimate sexual activities. Select 1 or more of the decisions you may face (such as whether or not to do certain things, whether or not to continue the relationship, or how to communicate your choices and values) and use a decision tree to work through the problem.

HAVING INPUT

You spend most of your free time with a friend you like very much. This person makes all of the decisions in your relationship. Although you agree with many of the decisions, you feel your input isn't important. Use a decision tree to work through ways you might change this situation.

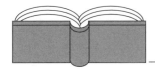

TYPES OF COMMUNICATION

STUDENT READING

Good communication skills are important in building positive self-esteem. People who are good communicators are likely to feel better about themselves, because they have better relationships with others. Communication may be either verbal or nonverbal.

VERBAL COMMUNICATION

When people talk, they generally use 4 levels of communication:

Level 1—Information giving
Level 2—Directive or sometimes argumentative
Level 3—Exploratory
Level 4—Self-disclosing

Level 1 communication is sociable, friendly, conventional and can be playful. It focuses on what people are thinking and does not provide for disclosure.

Level 2 communication involves directing, persuading, blaming, demanding, defending, praising, assuming, competing, evaluating, advising and withholding. It focuses on feeling, but has little disclosure.

Level 3 communication is tentative, it includes elaborating, exploring, speculating, searching, pondering, wondering, proposing and reflecting. It necessitates work, thinking and little disclosure.

Level 4 communication is aware, accepting, responsible, disclosing, responsive, understanding, caring and cooperative. It necessitates work, disclosure and sharing of feelings.

Conversations may contain all 4 levels of communication. Most people don't want to talk only on an emotional level (Level 4), because it can be draining. A Level 1 communication might be a question about how your sister's day was or how a friend's health is. Level 2 is clearly needed when a child wanders out into the street. Parents don't say,

"I think it would be in your best interest to stay out of the street"; they yell, "Get out of the street!"

When exploring interpersonal feelings, people usually use Level 3 communication. This way they can stay more safe. Suppose you ask someone you're dating how the relationship is going: "How do you feel about us? Do you think we can stay together?"

If your partner says, "Well, I really care about you and I want us to see each other a lot," then you can respond in a similar Level 4 fashion. But if your partner says, "I think we ought to date others," then you can respond, "I think so too." This is a Level 3 response, because even though it may hurt to say it, you are not admitting you are vulnerable to the other person.

Level 4 communication is daring but also more productive. It reveals who people really are because they state exactly how they feel. Self-disclosure means saying something such as, "I really care about you. I feel happy. The best times of my day are when I'm with you." This is taking a risk because the response can be positive or negative. If it is positive, then two people have become closer. If it is negative, the first person might feel hurt, but at least would know where things stand.

Couples often have Level 2 fights because of jealousy. One person might say, "I saw you look at him/her…" The other says, "I did not" (Level 2 denial). Then the couple has an argument.

Suppose a couple in this situation used Level 4 communication instead of the accusing Level 2. One of them might say, "I care about you and need you to care about me. I feel hurt inside when you seem to be attracted to others." This would be more productive. The other person cannot say, "I did not." He or she almost has to give a Level 4 response.

(continued…)

TYPES OF COMMUNICATION

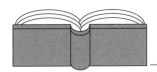

STUDENT READING, CONTINUED

NONVERBAL COMMUNICATION

Nonverbal communication may tell you even more than someone's words. Notice the body posture of your classmates. During an interesting lecture or activity, most of them will probably lean forward, showing that they are interested and involved. During a boring class, they will probably lean away from the lecturer or group. This physical behavior is called body language.

Body language often says as much as the spoken word. When people feel uncomfortable about expressing their thoughts or feelings verbally, body language is sometimes the only form of communication they will do.

We all recognize the importance of communicating nonverbally. We smile when we say hello. We scratch our heads when perplexed. We hug a friend to show affection. We even have terms that describe nonverbal behavior, such as "Keep a stiff upper lip," "I'm tongue-tied," and "He caught her eye."

We show whether we like or dislike something, or don't care about it, by our facial expressions and gestures. We can tell people we are interested in them just by making eye contact, and we show parts of our personality by the way we dress and even how we stand.

But nonverbal expressions of feelings and thoughts can be easy to misinterpret. So, depending just on nonverbal communication to express yourself is risky. You could be misunderstood.

COMMUNICATION PROBLEMS

Poor communication usually has these qualities:

- failure to listen
- an attempt to win
- inability to show understanding of another's viewpoint
- being rigid and unwilling to look at other solutions

Obvious problems, including conflicts and violence, can result from poor communication.

WHAT DO YOU SEE? (1)

Name _____ Date _____ Period _____

DIRECTIONS Describe the following design while you stand with your back to the class. The class cannot ask you questions.

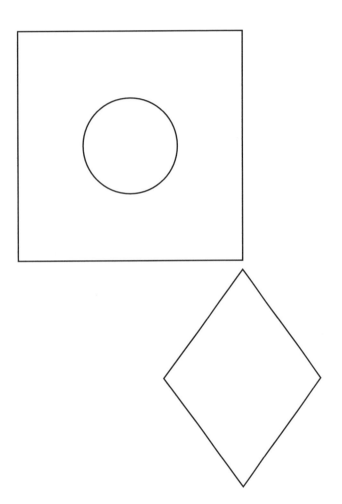

Choosing Health High School

WHAT DO YOU SEE? (2)

Name _____ Date _____ Period _____

 Describe the following design to the class. You may face them. They may ask you questions, but you cannot answer in words.

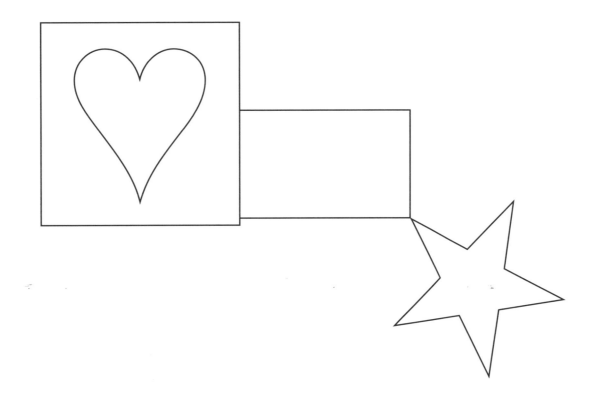

Choosing Health High School

WHAT DO YOU SEE? (3)

Name _____ Date _____ Period _____

DIRECTIONS ▶ Describe the following design to the class. They may ask you questions and you may answer.

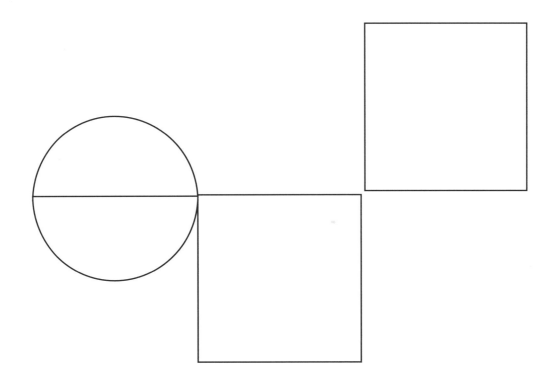

Choosing Health High School

The Communication Gap

Jim goes to the doctor because he is feeling pain when urinating. He describes the problem to his doctor, using slang terms that he learned from his friends. His doctor discusses the situation with him, but uses medical terms.

Jim doesn't understand most of these terms. Jim is too embarrassed to ask about the terms, so he leaves feeling frustrated.

1. What is the problem in this situation?

2. How could this communication problem have been avoided?

3. How could this situation have been improved?

Name _____ Date _____ Period _____

 **DIRECTIONS** Paul and Barbara are high school seniors. They have been dating for several months. Read the conversation and think about how Paul and Barbara could better arrive at a decision about Thanksgiving dinner.

Barbara: Thanksgiving is coming up, and I'd like you to have dinner with my family.

Paul: Now you ask! I've already told my folks to expect us for Thanksgiving dinner!

Barbara: You've got some nerve! You didn't even ask me if I wanted to go to your house for Thanksgiving dinner.

Paul: Ask you? You've been hitting the books so much lately that I've hardly seen you long enough to say hello, much less to ask you to Thanksgiving dinner.

Barbara: Would you rather have me fail my classes? You're pretty selfish.

Paul: I've had it! Either we're going to my house for Thanksgiving dinner or you can say good-bye right now.

Barbara: In that case, good-bye!

Adapted from: C. E. Bruess and J. S. Greenberg. 1988. *Sexuality Education.* New York: Macmillan Publishing Co.

SUCCESSFUL COMMUNICATION

Name _____ Date _____ Period _____

 **DIRECTIONS** Read the conversation and think about how Barbara and Paul arrive at their decision.

Barbara: Thanksgiving is coming up, and I'd like you to have dinner with my family.

Paul: Now you ask! I've already told my folks to expect us for Thanksgiving dinner!

Barbara: You thought I'd go to your house for Thanksgiving dinner?

Paul: Yes, and my parents are planning on it.

Barbara: Your parents would be upset if we canceled Thanksgiving dinner with them?

Paul: You bet! And I don't want to tell them we're not coming.

Barbara: I suppose you'd feel embarrassed about changing plans that your parents thought were definite.

Paul: Yes, I guess I would.

Barbara: It sounds like you were really looking forward to our being together at your house and with your family.

Paul: Yes, I really was.

Barbara: I'm glad you included me in your Thanksgiving plans, but I really was looking forward to spending this holiday with you at *my* family's house. And I'm a little bothered that you didn't consult me before making plans.

Paul: You have a point there. I'm sorry.

Barbara: Well, let's see if there are any alternatives we haven't considered.

Paul: We could spend half the day at my house and half at yours.

Barbara: Or we could invite your family to my house.

Paul: How about skipping Thanksgiving dinner with both families?

Barbara: If we spent half the day at each house, we'd waste a lot of time.

Paul: It's not realistic to expect my whole family to cancel their plans and go to your house.

Barbara: Well, if we didn't have dinner with either of them, both families would be disappointed.

Paul: Maybe we should all go out to dinner.

Barbara: That's an idea. I'll check with my parents tonight.

Paul: OK. I'll ask my family too.

Adapted from: C. E. Bruess and J. S. Greenberg. 1988. *Sexuality Education*. New York: MacMillan Publishing Co.

MEASURE YOUR ASSERTIVENESS

Name _____ Date _____ Period _____

DIRECTIONS Indicate how characteristic (like you or unlike you) and descriptive each of the following statements is of you by using the code given below.

(+3) very much like me, extremely descriptive
(+2) sort of like me, quite descriptive
(+1) a little like me, slightly descriptive
(−1) a little bit unlike me, slightly nondescriptive
(−2) sort of unlike me, quite nondescriptive
(−3) very much unlike me, extremely nondescriptive

_____ 1. Most people seem to be more aggressive and assertive than I am.

_____ 2. I have hesitated to make or accept dates because of "shyness."

_____ 3. When the food served at a restaurant isn't done to my satisfaction, I complain about it to the waiter or waitress.

_____ 4. I am careful to avoid hurting other people's feelings, even when I fell that I have been injured.

_____ 5. If a salesperson has gone to considerable trouble to show me merchandise which is not quite suitable, I have a difficult time in saying no.

_____ 6. When I am asked to do something, I insist upon knowing why.

_____ 7. There are times when I look for a good, vigorous argument.

_____ 8. I strive to get ahead as well as most people in my position.

_____ 9. To be honest, people often take advantage of me.

_____ 10. I enjoy starting conversations with new acquaintances and strangers.

_____ 11. I often don't know what to say to someone I find attractive.

_____ 12. I hesitate to make phone calls to business establishments and institutions.

_____ 13. I would rather apply for a job or for admission to a college by writing letters than by going through personal interviews.

_____ 14. I find it embarrassing to return merchandise.

_____ 15. If a close and respected relative were annoying me, I would smother my feelings rather than express my annoyance.

(continued...)

Choosing Health High School

CONTINUED

_____ 16. I have avoided asking questions for fear of sounding stupid.

_____ 17. During an argument I am sometimes afraid that I will get so upset that I'll shake all over.

_____ 18. If a famed and respected lecturer makes a statement which I think is incorrect, I will have the audience hear my point of view as well.

_____ 19. I avoid arguing over prices with clerks and salespeople.

_____ 20. When I have done something important or worthwhile, I manage to let others know about it.

_____ 21. I am open and frank about my feelings.

_____ 22. If someone has been spreading false and bad stories about me, I see him/her as soon as possible to "have a talk" about it.

_____ 23. I often have a hard time saying "no."

_____ 24. I tend to bottle up my emotions rather than make a scene.

_____ 25. I complain about poor service in a restaurant and elsewhere.

_____ 26. When I am given a compliment, I sometimes just don't know what to say.

_____ 27. If a couple near me in a theater were conversing rather loudly, I would ask them to be quiet or to take their conversation elsewhere.

_____ 28. Anyone attempting to push ahead of me in line is asking for a good battle.

_____ 29. I am quick to express an opinion.

_____ 30. There are times when I just can't say anything.

SCORING

First change the signs (+ or –) for items 1, 2, 4, 5, 9, 11, 12, 13, 14, 15, 16, 17, 19, 23, 24, 26, and 30. Next total the plus (+) items, then total the minus (–) items, and, lastly, subtract the minus total from the plus total to obtain your score. This score can range from –90 through zero to +90. The higher the score (closer to +90) the more assertively you usually behave. The lower the score (closer to –90) the more nonassertive is your typical behavior. (Note: This particular scale does not measure aggressiveness.)

Source: C. E. Bruess and J. S. Greenberg. 1988. *Sexuality Education*. New York: Macmillan Publishing Co.

© ETR Associates

Choosing Health High School

WHAT WOULD YOU SAY?

Name _____ Date _____ Period _____

Situation	Nonassertive response	Assertive response	Aggressive response
1. Someone is smoking in nonsmoking section you are sitting in and you don't like it.			
2. You order a cheeseburger and are served a hamburger. You are very unhappy.			
3. You're trying to study in your room and your sister is playing music so loud it distracts you.			
4. Write your own situation:			
5. Write your own situation:			
6. Write your own situation:			